Jack O'Connell

MORE'S UTOPIA

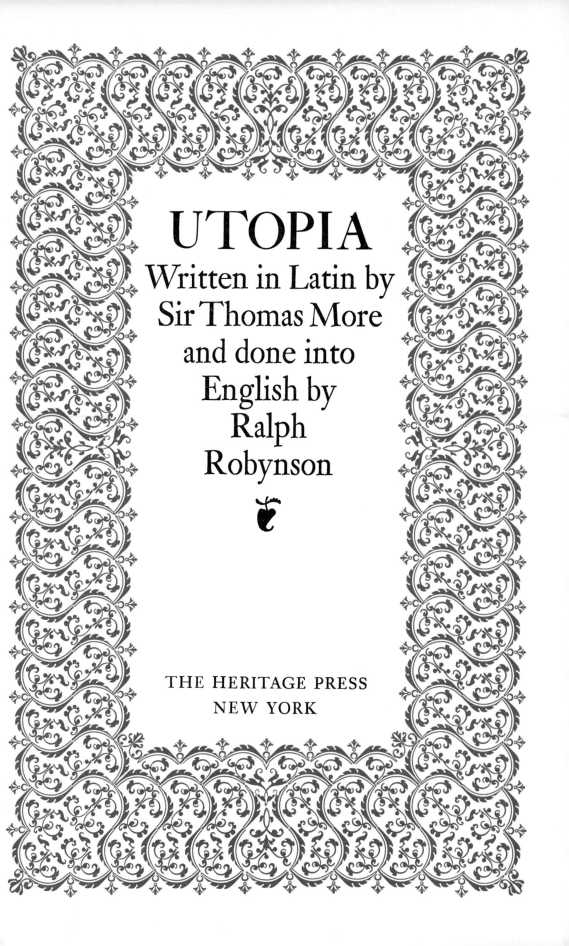

UTOPIA

Written in Latin by
Sir Thomas More
and done into
English by
Ralph
Robynson

THE HERITAGE PRESS
NEW YORK

PRINTED IN U.S.A.

INTRODUCTION

THERE are some writers who are chiefly interesting in themselves, and some whom chance and the agreement of men have picked out as symbols and convenient indications of some particular group or temperament of opinions. To the latter it is that Sir Thomas More belongs. An age and a type of mind have found in him and his *Utopia* a figurehead and a token; and pleasant and honourable as his personality and household present themselves to the modern reader, it is doubtful if they would by this time have retained any peculiar distinction among the many other contemporaries of whom we have chance glimpses in letters and suchlike documents, were it not that he happened to be the first man of affairs in England to imitate the *Republic* of Plato. By that chance it fell to him to give the world a noun and an adjective of abuse, "Utopian," and to record how under the stimulus of Plato's releasing influence the opening problems of our modern world presented themselves to the opening English mind of his time. For the most part the problems that exercised him are the problems that exercise us today; some of them, it may be, have grown up and intermarried, new ones have joined their company, but few, if any, have disappeared, and it is alike in his resemblances to, and differences from, the modern speculative mind that his essential interest lies.

The portrait presented by contemporary mention and his own intentional and unintentional admissions, is of an active-minded and agreeable-mannered man, a hard worker, very markedly prone to quips and whimsical sayings and plays upon words, and aware of a double reputation as a man of erudition and a wit. This latter quality it was that won him advancement at court, and it may have been his too clearly confessed reluctance to play the part of an informal table jester to his king that laid the grounds of that deepening royal resentment that ended only with his execution. But he was also valued by the king for more solid merits, he was needed by the king; and it was more than a table scorned or a clash of opinion upon the validity of divorce, it was a more general estrangement and avoidance of service that caused that fit of regal petulance by which he died.

It would seem that he began and ended his career in the orthodox religion and a general acquiescence in the ideas and customs of his time, and he played an honourable and acceptable part in that time; but his permanent interest lies not in his general conformity but in his incidental scepticism, in the fact that underlying the observances and recognised rules and limitations that give the texture of his life were the profoundest doubts, and that, stirred and disturbed by Plato, he saw fit to write them down. One may doubt if such scepticism is in itself unusual, whether any large proportion of great statesmen, great ecclesiastics, and administrators have escaped phases of destructive self-criticism, of destructive criticism of the principles upon which their general careers were framed. But few have made so public an admission as Sir Thomas More. A good Catholic undoubtedly he was, and yet we find him capable of conceiving a non-Christian community excelling all Christendom in wisdom and virtue; in practice his sense of conformity and orthodoxy was manifest enough, but in his *Utopia* he ventures to contemplate, and that not merely wistfully but with some confidence, the possibility of an absolute religious toleration.

The *Utopia* is none the less interesting because it is one of the most profoundly inconsistent of books. Never were the forms of Socialism and Communism animated by so entirely an Individualist soul. The hands are the hands of Plato, the wide-thinking Greek, but the voice is the voice of a humane, public-spirited but limited and very practical English gentleman who takes the inferiority of his inferiors for granted, dislikes friars and tramps and loafers and all undisciplined and unproductive people, and is ruler in his own household. He abounds in sound practical ideas—for the migration of harvesters, for the universality of gardens and the artificial incubation of eggs—and he sweeps aside all Plato's suggestion of the citizen woman as though it had never entered his mind. He had indeed the Whig temperament, and it manifested itself down even to the practice of reading aloud in company which still prevails among the more representative survivors of the Whig tradition. He argues ably against private property, but no thought of any such radicalism as the admission of those poor peons of his, with head half-shaved and glaring uniform against escape, to participation in ownership appears in his proposals. His communism is all for the convenience of his Syphogrants and Tranibores, those gentlemen of gravity and experience, lest one should swell up above the others. So, too, is the essential Whiggery of the limitation of the Prince's revenues. It is the very spirit of eighteenth-century Constitutionalism. And his Whiggery bears Utilitarianism instead of the vanity of a flower. Among his cities, all of a size, so that "he that knoweth one knoweth all," the Benthamite would have revised his sceptical theology and admitted the possibility of heaven.

Like any Whig, More exalted reason above the imagination at every point, and so he fails to understand the magic prestige of gold, making that beautiful metal into vessels of dishonour to urge his case against it; nor had he any perception of the charm of extravagance, for example, or the desirability of various clothing. The Utopians went all in coarse linen and undyed wool—why should the world be coloured?—and all the economy of labour and shortening of the working day was to no other end than to prolong the years of study and the joys of reading aloud, the simple satisfactions of the good boy at his lessons, to the very end of life. "In the institution of that weal publique this end is only and chiefly pretended and minded, that what time may possibly be spared from the necessary occupations and affairs of the commonwealth, all that the citizens should withdraw from the bodily service to the free liberty of the mind and garnishing of the same. For herein they suppose the felicity of this life to consist."

Indeed it is no paradox to say that the *Utopia*, which has by a conspiracy of accidents become a proverb for undisciplined fancifulness in social and political matters, is in reality a very unimaginative work. In that, next to the accident of its priority, lies the secret of its continuing interest. In some respects it is like one of those precious and delightful scrap-books people disinter in old country houses; its very poverty of synthetic power leaves its ingredients, the cuttings from and imitations of Plato, the recipe for the hatching of eggs, the stern resolutions against scoundrels and rough fellows, all the sharper and brighter. There will always be found people to read in it, over and above the countless multitudes who will continue ignorantly to use its name for everything most alien to More's essential quality.

H. G. WELLS

A NOTE ON THE TEXT

More's Utopia, written in Latin, was first issued at Louvain in 1516. The first translation into English was made by Ralph Robynson and published at London in 1551; a second edition, corrected and altered, came in 1556. This was the only English version until 1684, when Gilbert Burnet brought forth a new translation, generally recognized as being closer to the Latin but with little of the charm of Robynson's racy and picturesque English.

The present printing is intended for readers who desire to enjoy the Utopia of Sir Thomas More with a maximum of pleasure and a minimum of difficulty. Ralph Robynson's first edition is used for the text, with obvious errors and omissions corrected, and with marginal notes defining some of the more obscure words and phrases. Of the many pieces of prefatory matter available, only those which bear directly on the narrative have been included. The spelling and paragraphing have been modernized.

Thomas More to Peter Giles
sendeth Greeting.

I AM almost ashamed, right well-beloved Peter Giles, to send unto you this book of the Utopian commonwealth, well-nigh after a year's space, which I am sure you looked for within a month and a half. And no marvel; for you knew well enough that I was already disburdened of all the labor and study belonging to the invention in this work and that I had no need at all to trouble my brains about the disposition or conveyance of the matter; and therefore had herein nothing else to do but only to rehearse those things which you and I together heard Master Raphael tell and declare. Wherefore there was no cause why I should study to set forth the matter with eloquence, forasmuch as his talk could not be fine and eloquent, being first not studied for but sudden and unpremeditate, and then as you know, of a man better seen in the Greek language than in the Latin tongue; and my writing, the nigher it should approach to his homely, plain, and simple speech, so much the nigher should it go to the truth, which is the only mark whereunto I do and ought to direct all my travail and study herein.

I grant and confess, friend Peter, myself discharged of so much labor, having all these things ready done to my hand, that almost there was nothing left for me to do; else either the invention or the disposition of this matter might have required of a wit neither base neither at all unlearned, both some time and leisure and also some study. But if it were requisite and necessary that the matter should also have been written eloquently and not alone truly, of a surety that thing could I have performed by no time nor study. But now, seeing all these cares, stays, and lets were taken away, wherein else so much labor and study should have been employed, and that there remained no other thing for me to do but only to write plainly the matter as I heard it spoken, that indeed was a thing light and easy to be done. Howbeit, to the dispatching of this so little business my other cares and troubles did leave almost less than no leisure. Whiles I do daily bestow my time about law matters, some to plead, some to hear, some as an arbitrator with mine award to determine, some as an umpire or a judge with my sentence finally to discuss; whiles I go one way to see and visit my friend, another way about mine own private affairs; whiles I spend almost all the day abroad among other and the residue at home among mine own; I leave to myself, I mean to my book, no time.

For when I am come home I must commune with my wife, chat with my children, and talk with my servants; all the which things I reckon and account among business, forasmuch as they must of necessity be done; and done must they needs be, unless a man will be a stranger in his own house. And in any wise a man must so fashion and order his conditions and so appoint and dispose himself that he be merry, jocund, and pleasant among them whom either nature hath provided or chance hath made or he himself hath chosen to be the fellows and companions of his life; so that with too much gentle behavior and familiarity he do not mar them and, by too much sufferance of his servants make them his masters. Among these things now rehearsed stealeth away the day, the month, the year. When do I write them? And all this while have I spoken no word of sleep, neither yet of meat, which among a great number doth waste no less time than doth sleep, wherein almost half the lifetime of man creepeth away. I therefore do win and get only that time which I steal from sleep and meat; which time because it is very little, and yet somewhat it is, therefore have I once at the last, though it be long first, finished Utopia and have sent it to you, friend Peter, to read and peruse; to the intent that if anything have escaped me you might put me in remembrance of it. For though in this behalf I do not greatly mistrust myself (which would God I were somewhat in wit and learning as I am not all of the worst and dullest memory), yet have I not so great trust and confidence in it that I think nothing could fall out of my mind.

For John Clement, my boy, who, as you know, was there present with us, whom I suffer to be away from no talk wherein may be any profit or goodness (for out of this young bladed and new-shot-up corn, which hath already begun to spring up both in Latin and Greek learning, I look for plentiful increase at length of goodly ripe grain), he, I say, hath brought me into a great doubt. For whereas Hythloday, unless my memory fail me, said that the bridge of Amaurote, which goeth over the river of Anyder, is five hundred paces, that is to say, half a mile, in length; my John sayeth that two hundred of those paces must be plucked away, for that the river containeth there not above three hundred paces in breadth.

I pray you heartily call the matter to your remembrance, for if you agree with him I also will say as you say and confess myself deceived. But if you cannot remember the thing, then surely I will write as I have done and as mine own remembrance serveth me; for as I will take good heed that there be in my book nothing false, so, if there be anything in doubt, I will rather tell a lie than make a lie; because I had rather be good than wise.

Howbeit, this matter may easily be remedied, if you will take the pains to ask the question of Raphael himself, by word of mouth, if he be now with you, or else by your letters; which you must needs do for another doubt also, which hath chanced through whose fault I cannot tell, whether through mine or yours or Raphael's; for neither we remembered to enquire of him, nor he to tell us, in what part of that new world Utopia is situate. The which thing I had rather have spent no small sum of money than that it should thus have escaped us; as well for that I am ashamed to be ignorant in what sea that island standeth whereof I write so long a treatise, as also because there be with us certain men, and especially one devout and godly man, and a professor of divinity, who is exceeding desirous to go unto Utopia; not for a vain and curious desire to see news but to the intent he may further and increase our religion which is there already luckily begun. And that he may the better accomplish and perform this his good intent, he is minded to procure that he may be sent thither of the bishop, yea and that he himself may be made bishop of Utopia; being nothing scrupulous herein that he must obtain this bishopric with suit, for he counteth that a godly suit which proceedeth not of the desire of honor or lucre but only of a godly zeal.

Wherefore I most earnestly desire you, friend Peter, to talk with Hythloday, if you can, face to face, or else to write your letters to him; and so to work in this matter that in this my book there may neither anything be found which is untrue neither anything be lacking which is true. And I think verily it shall be well done that you show unto him the book itself, for if I have missed or failed in any point, or if any fault have escaped me, no man can so well correct and amend it as he can; and yet that can he not do unless he peruse and read over my book written. Moreover by this means shall you perceive whether he be well willing and content that I should undertake to put this work in writing. For if he be minded to publish and put forth his own labors and travails himself, perchance he would be loath, and so would I also, that in publishing the Utopian weal public I should prevent and take from him the flower and grace of the novelty of this his history.

Howbeit, to say the very truth, I am not yet fully determined with myself whether I will put forth my book or no. For the natures of men be so divers, the fantasies of some so wayward, their minds so unkind, their judgments so corrupt, that they which lead a merry and a jocund life, following their own sensual pleasures and carnal lusts, may seem to be in a much better state or case than they that vex and unquiet themselves with cares and study for the putting forth and publishing of some thing that may be either profit or pleasure to others; which nevertheless will disdainfully, scornfully, and unkindly accept the same. The most part of all be unlearned, and a great number hath learning in contempt. The rude and barbarous alloweth nothing but that which is very barbarous indeed. If it be one that hath a little smack of learning, he rejecteth as homely and common ware whatsoever is not stuffed full of old moth-eaten words, and that be worn out of use. Some there be that have pleasure only in old rusty antiquities, and some only in their own doings. One is so sour, so crabbed, and so unpleasant that he can away with no mirth nor sport. Another is so narrow in the shoulders that he can bear no jests nor taunts. Some silly poor souls be so afeared that at every snappish word their nose shall be bitten off that they stand in no less dread of every quick and sharp word than he that is bitten of a mad dog feareth water. Some be so mutable and wavering that every hour they be in a new mind, saying one thing sitting and another thing standing. Another sort sitteth upon their ale-benches and there among their cups they give judgment of the wits of writers and with great authority they condemn even as pleaseth them every writer according to his writing, in most spiteful manner mocking, louting, and flouting them; being themselves in the mean season safe and, as sayeth the proverb, out of all danger of gunshot; for why, they be so smug and smooth that they have not so much as one hair of an honest man whereby one may take hold of them. There be moreover some so unkind and ungentle that though they take great pleasure and delectation in the work, yet for all that they cannot find in their hearts to love the author thereof nor to afford him a good word; being much like uncourteous, unthankful, and churlish guests, which, when they have with good and dainty meats well filled their bellies, depart home, giving no thanks to the feast-maker. Go your ways now and make a costly feast at your own charges for guests so dainty-mouthed, so divers in taste, and besides that of so unkind and unthankful natures.

But nevertheless, friend Peter, do, I pray you, with Hythloday as I willed you before. And as for this matter, I shall be at my liberty afterwards to take new advisement. Howbeit, seeing I have taken great pains and labor in writing the matter, if it may stand with his mind and pleasure, I will, as touching the edition or publishing of the book, follow the counsel and advice of my friends, and specially yours. Thus fare you well, right heartily beloved friend Peter, with your gentle wife; and love me as you have ever done; for I love you better than ever I did.

John Clement   Raphael Hythloday   Sir Thos. More   Peter Giles

THE FIRST BOOK

of the communication of
Raphael Hythloday
concerning the
best state of a
common-
wealth

BOOK ONE

THE most victorious and triumphant King of England, Henry the eighth of that name, in all royal virtues prince most peerless, had of late in controversy with the right high and mighty King of Castile weighty matters, and of great importance; for the debatement and final determination whereof the King's Majesty sent me ambassador into Flanders, joined in commission with Cuthbert Tunstall, a man doubtless out of comparison, and whom the King's Majesty of late, to the great rejoicing of all men, did prefer to the office of Master of the Rolls. But of this man's praises I will say nothing; not because I do fear that small credence shall be given to the testimony that cometh out of a friend's mouth, but because his virtue and learning be greater and of more excellency than that I am able to praise them; and also in all places so famous and so perfectly well known that they need not nor ought not of me to be praised, unless I would seem to show and set forth the brightness of the sun with a candle, as the proverb sayeth.

There met us at Bruges (for thus it was before agreed) they whom their prince had for that matter appointed commissioners, excellent men all. The chief and the head

of them was the Margrave (as they call him) of Bruges,
a right honorable man: but the wisest and the best spoken of them was George Temsice, provost of Cassel, a
man not only by learning but also by nature of singular
eloquence, and in the laws profoundly learned; but in
reasoning and debating of matters, what by his natural
wit, and what by daily exercise, surely he had few fellows. After that we had once or twice met, and upon
certain points or articles could not fully and thoroughly
agree, they for a certain space took their leave of us, and
departed to Brussels, there to know their prince's pleasure. I in the meantime (for so my business lay) went
straight thence to Antwerp.

Whiles I was there abiding, often times among other,
but which to me was more welcome than any other, did
visit me one Peter Giles, a citizen of Antwerp; a man
there in his country of honest reputation, and also pre-
ferred to high promotions, worthy truly of the highest.
For it is hard to say whether the young man be in learning or in honesty more excellent. For he is both of
wonderful virtuous conditions, and also singularly well
learned, and towards all sorts of people exceeding gentle;
but towards his friends so kind hearted, so loving, so
faithful, so trusty, and of so earnest affection, that it
were very hard in any place to find a man that with him
in all points of friendship may be compared. No man
can be more lowly or courteous. No man useth less
simulation or dissimulation; in no man is more prudent
simplicity. Besides this, he is in his talk and communication so merry and pleasant, yea, and that without harm,
that, through his gentle entertainment and his sweet and
delectable communication, in me was greatly abated and
diminished the fervent desire that I had to see my native

country, my wife and my children; whom then I did much long and covet to see, because that at that time I had been more than four months from them.

Upon a certain day when I had heard the divine service in Our Lady's church, which is the fairest, the most gorgeous and curious church of building in all the city, and also most frequented of people, and the service being done, was ready to go home to my lodgings, I chanced to espy this foresaid Peter talking with a certain stranger, a man well stricken in age, with a black sunburned face, a long beard, and a cloak cast homely about his shoulders, whom by his favor and apparel forthwith I judged to be a mariner. But when this Peter saw me, he cometh to me and saluteth me. And as I was about to answer him, 'See you this man?' sayeth he (and therewith he pointed to the man that I saw him talking with before). 'I was minded,' quoth he, 'to bring him straight home to you.'

'He should have been very welcome to me,' said I, 'for your sake.'

'Nay,' (quoth he), 'for his own sake, if you knew him; for there is no man this day living that can tell you of so many strange and unknown peoples and countries as this man can. And I know well that you be very desirous to hear of such news.'

'Then I conjectured not far amiss,' (quoth I), 'for even at the first sight I judged him to be a mariner.'

'Nay,' (quoth he), 'there ye were greatly deceived. He hath sailed indeed, not as the mariner Palinure, but as the expert and prudent prince Ulysses; yea, rather as the ancient and sage Philosopher Plato. For this same Raphael Hythloday (for this is his name) is very well learned in the Latin tongue; but profound and excellent in the Greek tongue, wherein he ever bestowed more

study than in the Latin, because he had given himself
wholly to the study of philosophy, whereof he knew
that there is nothing extant in the Latin tongue that is
to any purpose, saving a few of Seneca's and Cicero's
doings. His patrimony that he was born unto he left to
his brethren (for he is a Portugal born); and for the
desire that he had to see and know the far countries of
the world, he joined himself in company with Amerigo
Vespucci, and in the three last voyages of those four that
be now in print and abroad in every man's hands, he
continued still in his company; saving that in the last
voyage he came not home again with him. For he made
such means and shift, what by entreatance and what by
importune suit, that he got license of Master Amerigo
(though it were sore against his will) to be one of the
twenty-four which in the end of the last voyage were
Gulike = Julich
(Juliers), mis-
translated from
Latin Castellum,
in castello = in a
fort
left in the country of Gulike. He was therefore left behind for his mind's sake, as one that took more thought
and care for traveling than dying; having customably
in his mouth these sayings: He that hath no grave is covered with the sky; and, The way to heaven out of all
places is of like length and distance; which fantasy of his
(if God had not been his better friend) he had surely
bought full dear.

'But after the departing of Master Vespucci, when he
had traveled through and about many countries, with
five of his companions, Gulikians, at the last by marvel-
Taprobane =
Ceylon
ous chance he arrived in Taprobane, from whence he
went to Calicut, where he chanced to find certain of his
country ships, wherein he returned again into his country, nothing less than looked for.'

All this when Peter had told me, I thanked him for
his gentle kindness, that he had vouchsafed to bring

me to the speech of that man whose communication he thought should be to me pleasant and acceptable. And therewith I turned me to Raphael; and when we had hailed the one the other, and had spoken these common words that be customably spoken at the first meeting and acquaintance of strangers, we went thence to my house, and there in my garden, upon a bench covered with green turfs, we sat down talking together.

There he told us how that, after the departing of Vespucci, he and his fellows that tarried behind in Gulike began by little and little, through fair and gentle speech, to win the love and favor of the people of that country; in so much that within short space they did dwell among them not only harmless, but also occupied with them very familiarly. He told us also that they were in high reputation and favor with a certain great man (whose name and country is now quite out of my remembrance), which of his mere liberality did bear the costs and charges of him and his five companions, and besides that gave them a trusty guide to conduct them in their journey (which by water was in boats and by land in wagons), and to bring them to other princes with very friendly commendations. Thus after many days' journeys, he said they found towns and cities, and weal publics full of people, governed by good and wholesome laws.

'For under the line equinoctial and of both sides of the same, as far as the sun doth extend his course, lieth' (quoth he) 'great and wide deserts and wildernesses, parched, burned and dried up with continual and intolerable heat. All things be hideous, terrible, loathesome, and unpleasant to behold; all things out of fashion and comeliness, inhabited with wild beasts and serpents, or at the leastwise with people that be no less savage, wild, and noisome than the very beasts themselves be. But a little farther beyond that all things begin by little and little to wax pleasant; the air soft, temperate, and gentle; the ground covered with green grass; less wildness in the beasts. At the last shall ye come again to people, cities, and towns, wherein is continual intercourse and occupying of merchandise and chaffer, not only among themselves and with their borderers, but also with merchants of far countries both by land and water.

'There I had occasion,' (said he) 'to go to many countries of every side. For there was no ship ready to any voyage or journey but I and my fellows were into it very gladly received.'

The ships that they found first were made plain, flat, and broad in the bottom, troughwise. The sails were made of great rushes, or of wickers, and in some places of leather. Afterward they found ships with ridged keels, and sails of canvas; yea, and shortly after having all things like ours; the shipmen also very expert and cunning both in the sea and in the weather. But he said that he found great favor and friendship among them for teaching them the feat and use of the lodestone, which to them before that time was unknown; and therefore they were wont to be very timorous and fearful upon the sea, nor to venture upon it but only in the summer time. But now they have such a confidence in that stone, that they fear not stormy winter; in so doing, farther from care than jeopardy; in so much that it is greatly to be doubted lest that thing, through their own foolish hardiness, shall turn then to evil and harm, which at the first was supposed should be to them good and commodious.

But what he told us that he saw in every country where he came, it were very long to declare. Neither it is my purpose at this time to make rehearsal thereof, but per-adventure in another place I will speak of it; chiefly such things as shall be profitable to be known; as in special be those decrees and ordinances that he marked to be well and wisely provided and enacted among such peoples as do live together in a civil policy and good order. For of such things did we busily enquire and demand of him, and he likewise very willingly told us of the same. But as for monsters, because they be no news, of them we were nothing inquisitive. For nothing is more easy to be found than be barking Scyllas, ravening Celenos, and Lestrygons, devourers of people, and such like great and incredible monsters; but to find citizens ruled by good and wholesome laws, that is an exceeding rare and hard thing.

But as he marked many fond and foolish laws in those new found lands, so he rehearsed many acts and consti-tutions whereby these our cities, nations, countries, and kingdoms may take ensample, to amend their faults, enormities and errors; whereof in another place, as I said, I will entreat. Now at this time I am determined to rehearse only that he told us of the manners, customs, laws, and ordinances of the Utopians.

But first I will repeat our former communication; by the occasion, and, as I might say, the drift whereof he was brought into the mention of that weal public. For when Raphael had very prudently touched divers things that be amiss, some here and some there; yea, very many of both parts; and again had spoken of such wise and prudent laws and decrees as be established and used both here among us and also there among them, as a man so cunning and expert in the laws and customs of every several country as though into what place soever he came guest-wise, there he had led all his life: then Peter, much marveling at the man, 'Surely Master Raphael' (quoth he), 'I wonder greatly why you get you not into some king's court; for I am sure there is no prince living that would not be very glad of you; as a man not only able highly to delight him with your profound learning, and this your knowledge of countries and peoples, but also are meet to instruct him with examples, and help him with counsel. And thus doing you shall bring yourself in a very good case, and also be in ability to help all your friends and kinsfolk.'

'As concerning my friends and kinsfolk' (quoth he), 'I pass not greatly for them; for I think I have sufficiently done my part towards them already. For these things that other men do not depart from until they be old and sick, yea, which they be then very loath to leave when they can no longer keep, those very same things did I, being not only lusty and in good health, but also in the flower of my youth, divide among my friends and kinsfolk; which I think with this my liberality ought to hold them contented, and not to require nor to look that besides this I should for their sakes give myself in bondage to kings.'

'Nay, God forbid' (quoth Peter), 'it is not my mind that you should be in bondage to kings, but as a retainer to them at your pleasure; which surely I think is the nighest way that you can devise how to bestow your time fruitfully, not only for the private commodity of your friends and for the general profit of all sorts of people, but also for the advancement of yourself to a much wealthier state and condition than you be now in.'

'To a wealthier condition' (quoth Raphael), 'by that means that my mind standeth clean against? Now I live at liberty, after mine own mind and pleasure; which I think very few of these great states and peers of realms can say. Yea, and there be enough of them that seek for great men's friendships; and therefore think it no great hurt if they have not me, nor two or three such other as I am.'

'Well, I perceive plainly, friend Raphael' (quoth I), 'that you be desirous neither of riches nor of power. And truly I have in no less reverence and estimation a man that is of your mind, than any of them all that be so high in power and authority. But you shall do as it becometh you, yea, and according to this wisdom and this high and free courage of yours, if you can find in your heart so to appoint and dispose yourself, that you may apply your wit and diligence to the profit of the weal public, though it be somewhat to your own pain and hindrance. And this shall you never so well do, nor with so great profit perform, as if you be of some great prince's council, and put into his head (as I doubt not but you will) honest opinions and virtuous persuasions. For from the prince, as from a perpetual well-spring, cometh among the people the flood of all that is good or evil. But in you is so perfect learning, that without any experience, and again so great experience, that without any learning, you may well be any king's counsellor.'

'You be twice deceived, Master More' (quoth he), 'first in me, and again in the thing itself. For neither is in me that ability that you force upon me; and if it were never so much, yet in disquieting mine own quietness I should nothing further the weal public. For, first of all, the most part of all princes have more delight in warlike matters and feats of chivalry (the knowledge whereof I neither have nor desire), than in the good feats of peace;

and employ much more study how by right or by wrong
to enlarge their dominions, than how well and peaceably to rule and govern that they have already. Moreover, they that be counsellors to kings, every one of them
either is of himself so wise indeed that he need not, or
else he thinketh himself so wise, that he will not allow
another man's counsel; saving that they do shamefully
and flatteringly give assent to the fond and foolish sayings of certain great men, whose favors, because they be
in high authority with their prince, by assentation and
flattering they labor to obtain. And verily it is naturally
given to all men to esteem their own intentions best. So
both the raven and the ape think their own young ones
fairest.

'Then if a man in such a company, where some dis-
dain and have despite at other men's inventions, and
some count their own best, if among such men, I say, a
man should bring forth anything that he hath read done
in times past, or that he hath seen done in other places,
there the hearers fare as though the whole estimation
of their wisdom were in jeopardy to be overthrown,
and that ever after they should be counted for very dis-
diserdes =fools erdes, unless they could in other men's inventions pick
out matter to reprehend and find fault at. If all other
poor helps fail, then this is their extreme refuge: "These
things" (say they) "pleased our forefathers and ancestors: would God we could be so wise as they were." And
as though they had wittily concluded the matter and
with this answer stopped every man's mouth, they sit
down again; as who should say it were a very dangerous
matter if a man in any point should be found wiser than
his forefathers were. And yet be we content to suffer
the best and wittiest of their decrees to lie unexecuted;

but if in anything a better order might have been taken than by them was, there we take fast hold and find many faults. Many times have I chanced upon such proud, lewd, overthwart, and wayward judgments; yea, and once in England.' 'I pray you' (quoth I), 'have you been in our country?'

lewd = foolish

'Yea, forsooth,' (quoth he), 'and there I tarried for the space of four or five months together, not long after the insurrection that the western Englishmen made against their king; which by their own miserable and pitiful slaughter was suppressed and ended. In the mean season I was much bound and beholden to the right reverend father John Morton, Archbishop, and Cardinal of Canterbury, and at that time also Lord Chancellor of England; a man, Master Peter (for Master More knoweth already that I will say), not more honorable for his authority than for his prudence and virtue. He was of a mean stature, and though stricken in age yet bore he his body upright. In his face did shine such an amiable reverence as was pleasant to behold. Gentle in communication, yet earnest and sage, he had great delight many times with rough speech to his suitors to prove, but without harm, what prompt wit and what bold spirit were in every man, in the which, as in a virtue much agreeing with his nature, so that therewith were not joined impudency, he took great delectation; and the same person, as apt and meet to have an administration in the weal public, he did lovingly embrace. In his speech he was fine, eloquent, and pithy. In the law he had profound knowledge; in wit he was incomparable; and in memory wonderful excellent. These qualities, which in him were by nature singular, he by learning and use had made perfect.

'The King put much trust in his counsel: the weal public also in a manner leaned unto him, when I was there. For even in the chief of his youth he was taken from school into the Court, and there passed all his time in much trouble and business, and was continually tumbled and tossed in the waves of divers misfortunes and adversities. And so by many and great dangers he learned the experience of the world, which so being learned cannot easily be forgotten.

'It chanced on a certain day, when I sat at his table, there was also a certain layman, cunning in the laws of your realm, which, I cannot tell whereof taking occasion, began diligently and busily to praise that strait and rigorous justice which at that time was there executed upon felons, who, as he said, were for the most part twenty hanged together upon one gallows. And, seeing so few escaped punishment, he said he could not choose but greatly wonder and marvel, how and by what evil luck it should so come to pass that these nevertheless were in every place so rife and rank. "Nay, sir," quoth I (for I durst boldly speak my mind before the Cardinal), "marvel nothing hereat; for this punishment of thieves passeth the limits [of] justice, and is also very hurtful to the weal public. For it is too extreme and cruel a punishment for theft, and yet not sufficient to refrain men from theft. For simple theft is not so great an offence that it ought to be punished with death. Neither there is any punishment so horrible that it can keep them from stealing which have no other craft whereby to get their living. Therefore in this point, not you only, but also the most part of the world be like evil schoolmasters, which be readier to beat than to teach their scholars. For great and horrible punishments be appointed for thieves;

whereas much rather provision should have been made that there were some means whereby they might get their living, so that no man should be driven to this extreme necessity, first to steal, and then to die." "Yes" (quoth he), "this matter is well enough provided for already. There be handicrafts, there is husbandry to get their living by, if they would not willingly be naught." "Nay" (quoth I), "you shall not scape so; for, first of all, I will speak nothing of them that come home out of war maimed and lame, as not long ago out of Blackheath field, and a little before that out of the wars in France: such (I say) as put their lives in jeopardy for the weal public's or the king's sake, and by the reason of weakness and lameness be not able to occupy their old crafts, and be too aged to learn new: of them I will speak nothing, because war like the tide ebbeth and floweth. But let us consider those things that chance daily before our eyes.

' "First, there is a great number of gentlemen, which cannot be content to live idle themselves, like dors, of that which other have labored for: their tenants I mean, whom they poll and shave to the quick by raising their rents (for this only point of frugality do they use, men else through their lavish and prodigal spending able to bring themselves to very beggary): these gentlemen (I say) do not only live in idleness themselves, but also carry about with them at their tails a great flock or train of idle and loitering serving-men, which never learned any craft whereby to get their livings. These men, as soon as their master is dead, or be sick themselves, be incontinent thrust out of doors. For gentlemen had rather keep idle persons than sick men; and many times the dead man's heir is not able to maintain so great a house, and keep so many serving-men as his father did.

dors = drones

Then in the mean season they that be thus destitute of service either starve for hunger or manfully play the thieves. For what would you have them to do? When they have wandered abroad so long, until they have worn threadbare their apparel, and also appaired their health, then gentlemen, because of their pale and sick faces and patched coats, will not take them into service. And husbandmen dare not set them a-work, knowing well enough that he is nothing meet to do true and faithful service to a poor man with a spade and a mattock, for small wages and hard fare, which, being daintily and tenderly pampered up in idleness and pleasure, was wont *jet = strut* with a sword and a buckler by his side to jet through the street with a bragging look, and to think himself too good to be any man's mate."

' "Nay, by Saint Mary, sir," (quoth the lawyer), "not so, for this kind of men must we make most of. For in them, as men of stouter stomachs, bolder spirits, and manlier courages, than handicraftsmen and plowmen be, doth consist the whole power, strength, and puissance of our host when we must fight in battle."

' "Forsooth, sir, as well you might say" (quoth I), "that for war's sake you must cherish thieves. For surely you shall never lack thieves whiles you have them. No, nor thieves be not the most false and faint hearted soldiers, nor soldiers be not the cowardliest thieves; so well these two crafts agree together. But this fault, though it be much used among you, yet is it not peculiar to you only, but common also almost to all nations. Yet France, besides this, is troubled and infected with a much sorer plague. The whole realm is filled and besieged with hired soldiers in peace time, if that be peace; which be brought in under the same color and pretence, that hath persuaded you to keep these idle serving-men. For these wise-fools and very arch-dolts thought the wealth of the whole country herein to consist, if there were ever in a readiness a strong and a sure garrison, specially of old practised soldiers; for they put no trust at all in men unexercised. And therefore they must be fain to seek for war, to the end they may ever have practised soldiers and cunning manslayers; lest that (as it is prettily said of Sallust) their hands and their minds through idleness or lack of exercise should wax dull.

' "But how pernicious and pestilent a thing it is to maintain such beasts, the Frenchmen by their own harms have learned; and the examples of the Romans, Carthaginians, Syrians and of many other countries, do manifestly declare. For not only the empire, but also the fields and cities of all these, by divers occasions have been overrun and destroyed of their own armies beforehand had in a readiness. Now how unnecessary a thing this is, hereby it may appear: that the French soldiers, which from their youth have been practised and inured in feats of arms, do not crack nor advance themselves to have very often got the upper hand and mastery of your new made and unpractised soldiers. But in this point I will not use many words, lest perchance I may seem to flatter you. No, nor those same handicraft men of yours in cities, nor yet the rude and uplandish plowmen of the country, are not supposed to be greatly afraid of your gentlemen's idle serving-men, unless it be such as be not of body or stature correspondent to their strength and courage; or else whose bold stomachs be discouraged through poverty. Thus you may see that it is not to be feared lest they should be effeminated if they were brought up in good crafts and laborsome works whereby to get their living; whose stout and sturdy bodies (for gentlemen vouchsafe to corrupt and spill none but picked and chosen men) now either by reason of rest and idleness, be brought to weakness, or else by too easy and womanly exercises be made feeble and unable to endure hardness. Truly, howsoever the case standeth, this methinketh is nothing available to the weal public, for war's sake, which you never have but when you will yourselves, to keep and maintain an innumerable flock of that sort of men that be so troublesome and noyous in peace; whereof you ought to have a thousand times more regard than of war.

' "But yet this is not only the necessary cause of stealing. There is another which, as I suppose, is proper and peculiar to you Englishmen alone." "What is that?" quoth the Cardinal. "Forsooth," (quoth I), "your sheep, that were wont to be so meek and tame, and so small eaters, now, as I hear say, be become so great devourers, and so wild, that they eat up and swallow down the very men themselves. They consume, destroy, and devour whole fields, houses, and cities. For look in what parts of the realm doth grow the finest, and therefore dearest wool, there noblemen and gentlemen, yea, and certain abbots, holy men, God wot, not contenting themselves with the yearly revenues and profits that were wont to grow to their forefathers and predecessors of their lands, nor being content that they live in rest and pleasure, nothing profiting, yea, much noying the weal public, leave no ground for tillage; they enclose all in pastures; they throw down houses; they pluck down towns; and leave nothing standing but only the church, to make of it a sheep-house. And, as though you lost no small quantity of ground by forests, chases, lawns and parks, those good holy men turn all dwelling places and all glebe land into desolation and wilderness.

' "Therefore, that one covetous and insatiable cormorant and very plague of his native country may compass about and enclose many thousand acres of ground together within one pale or hedge, the husbandmen be thrust out of their own; or else either by covin or fraud, *covin = deceit* or by violent oppression, they be put besides it, or by wrongs and injuries they be so wearied that they be compelled to sell all. By one means therefore or by other, either by hook or crook, they must needs depart away, poor, silly, wretched souls; men, women, husbands, wives, fatherless children, widows, woeful mothers with their young babes, and their whole household, small in substance and much in number, as husbandry requireth many hands. Away they trudge, I say, out of their known and accustomed houses, finding no places to rest in. All their household stuff, which is very little worth, though it might well abide the sale, yet being suddenly thrust out, they be constrained to sell it for a thing of naught. And when they have, wandering about, soon spent that, what can they else do but steal, and then justly, God wot, be hanged, or else go about a-begging? And yet then also they be cast in prison as vagabonds, because they go about and work not; whom no man will set a-work, though they never so willingly offer themselves thereto. For one shepherd or herdman is enough to eat up that ground with cattle, to the occupying whereof about husbandry many hands were requisite.

' "And this is also the cause that victuals be now in many places dearer. Yea, besides this the price of wool is so risen that poor folks, which were wont to work it and make cloth of it, be now able to buy none at all. And by this means very many be fain to forsake work and to give themselves to idleness. For after that so much ground was enclosed for pasture, an infinite multitude of sheep died of the rot, such vengeance God took of their inordinate and insatiable covetousness, sending among the sheep that pestiferous murrain, which much more justly should have fallen on the sheep-masters' own heads. And though the number of sheep increase never so fast, yet the price falleth not one mite, because there be so few sellers. For they be almost all come into a few rich men's hands, whom no need driveth to sell before they lust; and they lust not before they may sell as dear as they lust. Now the same cause bringeth in like dearth of the other kinds of cattle; yea, and that so much the more, because that after farms plucked down and husbandry decayed there is no man that passeth for the breeding of young store. For these rich men bring not up the young ones of great cattle as they do lambs, but first they buy them abroad very cheap, and afterward, when they be fatted in their pastures, they sell them again exceeding dear. And therefore (as I suppose) the whole incommodity hereof is not yet felt. For yet they make dearth only in those places where they sell. But when they shall fetch them away from thence where they be bred, faster than they can be brought up, then shall there also be felt great dearth, when store beginneth to fail there where the ware is bought.

' "Thus the unreasonable covetousness of a few hath turned that thing to the utter undoing of your island, in the which thing the chief felicity of your realm did consist. For this great dearth of victuals causeth every man to keep as little houses and as small hospitality as he possible may, and to put away their servants: whither, I pray you, but a-begging? or else, which these gentle bloods and stout stomachs will sooner set their minds unto, a-stealing?

' "Now, to amend the matters, to this wretched beggary and miserable poverty is joined great wantonness, importunate superfluity, and excessive riot. For not only gentlemen's servants but also handicraft men, yea, and almost all the plowmen of the country, with all other sorts of people, use much strange and proud newfangleness in their apparel and too much prodigal riot and sumptuous fare at their table. Now bawds, queans, whores, harlots, strumpets, brothel-houses, stews, and yet another stews, wine taverns, ale houses, and tippling houses, with so many naughty lewd and unlawful games, as dice, cards, table tennis, bowls, quoits—do not all these send the haunters of them straight a-stealing when their money is gone?

' "Cast out these pernicious abominations. Make a law that they which plucked down farms and towns of husbandry, shall build them up again or else yield and uprender the possession of them to such as will go to the cost of building them anew. Suffer not these rich men to buy up all, to engross and forestall, and with their monopoly to keep the market alone as please them. Let not so many be brought up in idleness; let husbandry and tillage be restored again; let cloth working be renewed; that there may be honest labors for this idle sort to pass their time in profitably, which hitherto either poverty hath caused to be thieves, or else now be either vagabonds or idle serving men, and shortly will be thieves. Doubtless, unless you find a remedy for these enormities, you shall in vain advance yourselves of executing justice upon felons. For this justice is more beautiful than just or profitable. For by suffering your youth wantonly and viciously to be brought up, and to be infected even from their tender age by little and little with vice, then, a God's name, to be punished when they commit the same faults after they be come to man's state, which from their youth they were ever like to do — in this point, I pray you, what other thing do you than make thieves and then punish them?"

'Now as I was thus speaking, the lawyer began to make himself ready to answer, and was determined with himself to use the common fashion and trade of disputers, which be more diligent in rehearsing than answering, as thinking the memory worthy of the chief praise. "Indeed, sir" (quoth he), "you have said well, being but a stranger, and one that might rather hear something of these matters than have any exact or perfect knowledge of the same, as I will incontinent by open proof make manifest and plain. For first I will rehearse in order all that you have said; then I will declare in what thing you be deceived, through lack of knowledge, in all our fashions, manners and customs; and last of all I will answer to your arguments and confute them every one. First therefore I will begin where I promised. Four things you seemed to me" — "Hold your peace" (quoth the cardinal), "for belike you will make no short answer, which make such a beginning; wherefore at this time you shall not take the pains to make your answer, but keep it to your next meeting, which I would be right glad that it might be even tomorrow next (unless either you or Master Raphael have any earnest let).

' "But now, Master Raphael, I would very gladly hear of you why you think theft not worthy to be punished with death; or what other punishment you can devise more expedient to the weal public. For I am sure you are not of that mind that you would have theft escape unpunished. For if now the extreme punishment of death cannot cause them to leave stealing, then if ruffians and robbers should be sure of their lives, what violence, what fear were able to hold their hands from robbing, which would take the mitigation of the punishment as a very provocation to the mischief?"

' "Surely, my lord" (quoth I), ' "I think it no right nor justice that the loss of money should cause the loss of man's life. For mine opinion is that all the goods in the world are not able to countervail man's life. But if they would thus say: that the breaking of justice, and the transgression of the laws is recompensed with this punishment, and not the loss of the money, then why may not this extreme justice well be called extreme injury? For neither so cruel governance, so strait rules and unmerciful laws be allowable, that if a small offence be committed, by and by the sword should be drawn; nor so stoical ordinances are to be borne withal, as to count all offences of such equality that the killing of a man or the taking of his money from him were both a matter, and the one no more heinous offence than the other: between the which two, if we have any respect to equity, no similitude or equality consisteth. God commandeth us that we shall not kill. And be we then so hasty to kill a man for taking a little money? And if any man would understand killing by this commandment of God to be forbidden after no larger wise than man's constitutions defineth killing to be lawful, then why may it not likewise by man's constitutions be determined after what sort whoredom, fornication, and perjury may be lawful? For whereas by the permission of God no man hath power to kill neither himself nor yet any other man, then if a law made by the consent of men concerning slaughter of men ought to be of such strength, force, and virtue, that they which contrary to the commandment of God have killed those whom this constitution of man commanded to be killed, be clean quit and exempt out of the bonds and danger of God's commandment; shall it not then by this reason follow that the power of God's commandment shall extend no further than man's law doth define and permit? And so shall it come to pass that in like manner man's constitutions in all things shall determine how far the observation of all God's commandments shall extend. To be short, Moses' law, though it were ungentle and sharp, as a law that was given to bondmen—yea, and them very obstinate, stubborn, and stiff-necked—yet it punished theft by the purse and not with death. And let us not think that God in the new law of clemency and mercy, under the which He ruleth us with fatherly gentleness as His dear children, hath given us greater scope and license to execute cruelty one upon another.

' "Now ye have heard the reasons whereby I am persuaded that this punishment is unlawful. Furthermore I think there is nobody that knoweth not how unreasonable, yea how pernicious a thing it is to the weal public that a thief and a homicide or murderer should suffer equal and like punishment. For the thief, seeing that man that is condemned for theft in no less jeopardy nor judged to no less punishment than him that is convict of manslaughter, through this cogitation only he is strongly and forcibly provoked, and in a manner constrained, to kill him whom else he would have but robbed. For, the murder once done, he is in less care and in more hope that the deed shall not be betrayed or known, seeing the party is now dead and rid out of the way, which only might have uttered and disclosed it. But if he chance to be taken and descried, yet he is in no more danger and jeopardy than if he had committed but single felony. Therefore whiles we go about with such cruelty to make thieves afeared, we provoke them to kill good men.

' "Now as touching this question, what punishment were more commodious and better; that truly in my judgment is easier to be found than what punishment were worse. For why should we doubt that to be a good and a profitable way for the punishment of offenders which we know did in times past so long please the Romans, men in the administration of a weal public most expert, politic, and cunning? Such as among them were convict of great and heinous trespasses, them they condemned into stone quarries, and into mines to dig metal, there to be kept in chains all the days of their life.

' "But as concerning this matter, I allow the ordinance of no nation so well as that I saw (whiles I traveled abroad about the world) used in Persia, among the people that commonly be called the Polylerites; whose land is both large and ample and also well and wittily governed, and the people in all conditions free and ruled by their own laws, saving that they pay a yearly tribute to the great king of Persia. But because they be far from the sea, compassed and closed in almost round about with high mountains and do content themselves with the fruits of their own land which is of itself very fertile and fruitful: for this cause neither they go to other countries nor other come to them. And according to the

Polylerites; from πολὺς λῆρος = much nonsense

old custom of the land, they desire not to enlarge the
bounds of their dominions; and those that they have by
reason of the high hills be easily defended; and the tribute which they pay to their chief lord and king setteth
them quit and free from warfare. Thus their life is commodious rather than gallant, and may better be called
happy or lucky than notable or famous. For they be
not known as much as by name, I suppose, saving only
to their next neighbors and borderers.

' "They that in this land be attainted and convict of
felony make restitution of that they stole to the right
owner, and not (as they do in other lands) to the king,
whom they think to have no more right to the thief-
stolen thing than the thief himself hath. But if the thing
be lost or made away, then the value of it is paid of the
goods of such offenders, which else remaineth all whole
to their wives and children. And they themselves be
condemned to be common laborers; and unless the theft
be very heinous, they be neither locked in prison, nor
fettered in gyves, but be united and go at large, laboring in the common works. They that refuse labor or go
slowly and slackly to their work, be not only tied in
chains but also pricked forward with stripes. They that
be diligent about their work live without check or rebuke. Every night they be called in by name and be
locked in their chambers. Beside their daily labor, their
life is nothing hard or incommodious. Their fare is indifferent good, borne at the charges of the weal public,
because they be common servants to the commonwealth.
But their charges in all places of the land is not borne
alike; for in some parts that is bestowed upon them is
gathered of alms. And though that may be uncertain,
yet the people be so full of mercy and pity, that none is

found more profitable or plentiful. In some places certain lands be appointed hereunto, of the revenues whereof they be maintained. And in some places every man giveth a certain tribute for the same use and purpose. Again in some parts of the land these serving-men (for so be these damned persons called) do no common work, but as every private man needeth laborers, so he cometh into the market-place, and there hireth some of them for meat and drink and a certain limited wages by the day, somewhat cheaper than he should hire a free man. It is also lawful for them to chastise the sloth of these serving-men with stripes.

' "By this means they never lack work, and besides their meat and drink every one of them bringeth daily something into the common treasury. All and every one of them be apparelled in one color. Their heads be not polled or shaven, but rounded a little above the ears; and the tip of the one ear is cut off. Every one of them may take meat and drink of their friends, and also a coat of their own color; but to receive money is death, as well to the giver as to the receiver. And no less jeopardy it is for a free man to receive money of a serving-man for any manner of cause; and likewise for serving-men to touch weapons. The serving-men of every several shire be distinct and known from other by their several and distinct badges, which to cast away is death; as it is also to be seen out of the precinct of their own shire, or to talk with a serving-man of another shire. And it is no less danger to them for to intend to run away than to do it indeed. Yea, and to conceal such an enterprise in a serving-man it is death; in a free man servitude. Of the contrary part, to him that openeth and uttereth such counsels be decreed large gifts; to a free man a great

sum of money; to a serving-man, freedom; and to them
both forgiveness and pardon of that they were of counsel in that pretence. So that it can never be so good for
them to go forward in their evil purpose as by repentance to turn back.

' "This is the law and order in this behalf, as I have
showed you; wherein what humanity is used, how far
it is from cruelty, and how commodious it is, you do
plainly perceive; for as much as the end of their wrath
and punishment intendeth nothing else but the destruction of vices and saving of men, with so using and ordering them that they cannot choose but be good; and what
harm soever they did before, in the residue of their life
to make amends for the same.

' "Moreover it is so little feared that they should turn
again to their vicious conditions that wayfaring men will
for their safeguard choose them to their guides before
any other, in every shire changing and taking new. For
if they would commit robbery, they have nothing about
them meet for that purpose. They may touch no weapons; money found about them should betray the robbery. They should be no sooner taken with the manner,
but forthwith they should be punished. Neither they
can have any hope at all to escape away by flying. For
how should a man that in no part of his apparel is like
other men, fly privily and unknown unless he would
run away naked? Howbeit, so also flying, he should be
descried by his rounding and his ear-mark. But it is a
thing to be doubted, that they will lay their heads together and conspire against the weal public. No, no, I
warrant you. For the serving-men of one shire alone
could never hope to bring to pass such an enterprise
without soliciting, enticing, and alluring the serving-

men of many other shires to take their parts. Which thing is to them so impossible that they may not as much as speak or talk together, or salute one another. No, it is not to be thought that they would make their own countrymen and companions of their counsel in such a matter which they know well should be jeopardy to the concealer thereof, and great commodity and goodness to the opener of the same: whereas on the other part, there is none of them all hopeless or in despair to recover again his freedom by humble obedience, by patient suffering, and by giving good tokens and likelihood of himself that he will ever after that live like a true and an honest man. For every year divers be restored again to their freedom through the commendation of their patience."

'When I had thus spoken, saying moreover that I could see no cause why this order might not be had in England with much more profit than the justice which the lawyer so highly praised, "Nay" (quoth the lawyer), "this could never be so stablished in England but that it must needs bring the weal public into great jeopardy and hazard." And as he was thus saying he shook his head and made a wry mouth, and so held his peace. And all that were there present with one assent agreed to his saying.

' "Well," (quoth the cardinal), "yet it were hard to judge without a proof whether this order would do well here or no. But when the sentence of death is given, if then the king should command execution to be deferred and spared, and would prove this order and fashion, taking away the privileges of all sanctuaries; if then the proof would declare the thing to be good and profitable, then it were well done that it were stablished. Else the condemned and reprieved persons may as well and as justly be put to death after this proof as when they were first cast. Neither any jeopardy can in the mean space grow hereof. Yea, and me thinketh that these vagabonds may very well be ordered after the same fashion, against whom we have hitherto made so many laws and so little prevailed."

'When the cardinal had thus said, then every man gave great praise to my sayings, which a little before they had disallowed. But most of all was esteemed that which was spoken of vagabonds, because it was the cardinal's own addition.

'I cannot tell whether it were best to rehearse the communication that followed, for it was not very sad. But yet you shall hear it, for there was no evil in it and partly it pertained to the matter before said.

'There chanced to stand by a certain jesting parasite, or scoffer, which would seem to resemble and counterfeit the fool. But he did in such wise counterfeit that he was almost the very same indeed that he labored to represent. He so studied with words and sayings brought forth so out of time and place to make sport and move laughter, that he himself was oftener laughed at than his jests were. Yet the foolish fellow brought out now and then such indifferent and reasonable stuff that he made the proverb true, which sayeth: He that shooteth oft, at the last shall hit the mark. So that when one of the company said that through my communication a good order was found for thieves, and that the cardinal also had well provided for vagabonds; so that only remained some good provision to be made for them that through sickness and age were fallen into poverty and were become so impotent and unwieldy that they were not able to work for their living: "Tush," (quoth he), "let me alone with them; you shall see me do well enough with them. For I had rather than any good that this kind of people were driven somewhither out of my sight: they have so sore troubled me many times and oft when they have with their lamentable tears begged money of me; and yet they could never to my mind so tune their song that thereby they ever got of me one farthing. For evermore the one of these two chanced: either that I would not, or else that I could not, because I had it not. Therefore now they be waxed wise. When they see me go by, because they will not lose their labor, they let me go, and say not one word to me. So they look for nothing of me; no, in good sooth, no more than if I were a priest. But I will make a law that all these beggars shall be distributed and bestowed into houses of religion. The men shall be made lay brethren, as they call them, and the women nuns." Hereat the cardinal smiled, and allowed it in jest; yea, and all the residue in good earnest.

'But a certain friar, graduate in divinity, took such pleasure and delight in this jest of priests and monks that he also, being else a man of grisly and stern gravity, began merrily and wantonly to jest and taunt. "Nay," (quoth he), "you shall not be so rid and dispatched of beggars unless you make some provision also for us friars." "Why" (quoth the jester), "that is done already. For my lord himself set a very good order for you when he decreed that vagabonds should be kept strait and set to work, for you be the greatest and veriest vagabonds that be."

'This jest also, when they saw the cardinal not disprove it, every man took it gladly, saving only the friar. For he (and that no marvel) when he was thus touched on the quick and hit on the gall, so fret, so fumed and chafed at it, and was in such a rage that he could not refrain himself from chiding, scolding, railing, and reviling. He called the fellow ribald, villain, javel, backbiter, slanderer, and the son of perdition; citing therewith terrible threatening out of holy scripture. Then the jesting scoffer began to play the scoffer indeed, and verily he was good at it, for he could play a part in that play, no man better. "Patient yourself, good master friar" (quoth he), "and be not angry; for scripture saith: In your patience you shall save your souls." Then the friar (for I will rehearse his own very words): "No, gallows-wretch, I am not angry" (quoth he); "or at the leastwise I do not sin, for the Psalmist saith: Be you angry and sin not."

javel = rascal

'Then the cardinal spake gently to the friar, and desired him to quiet himself. "No, my lord" (quoth he), "I speak not but of a good zeal as I ought; for holy men had a good zeal. Wherefore it is said, The zeal of thy house hath eaten me. And it is sung in the church: The scorners of Helizeus, whiles he went up into the house of God, felt the zeal of the bald; as peradventure this scorning villain ribald shall feel." "You do it" (quoth the cardinal) "perchance of a good mind and affection. But me thinketh you should do, I cannot tell whether more holily, certes more wisely, if you would not set your wit to a fool's wit and with a fool take in hand a foolish contention." "No, forsooth, my lord," (quoth he), "I should not do more wisely. For Solomon the wise sayeth: Answer a fool according to his foolishness; like as I do now, and do show him the pit that he shall fall into if he take not heed. For if many scorners of Helizeus, which was but one bald man, felt the zeal of the bald, how much more shall one scorner of many friars feel, among whom be many bald men? And we have also the Pope's bulls, whereby all that mock and scorn us be excommunicated, suspended, and accursed." The cardinal seeing that none end would be made, sent away the jester by a privy beck, and turned the communication to another matter. Shortly after, when he was risen from the table, he went to hear his suitors, and so dismissed us.

'Look, Master More, with how long and tedious a tale I have kept you, which surely I would have been ashamed to have done but that you so earnestly desired me, and did after such a sort give ear unto it, as though you would not that any parcel of that communication should be left out; which though I have done somewhat briefly, yet could I not choose but rehearse it, for the judgment of them, which, when they had improved and disallowed my sayings, yet incontinent hearing the cardinal allow them, did themselves also approve the same; so impudently flattering him that they were nothing ashamed to admit, yea, almost in good earnest, his jester's foolish inventions; because that he himself, by smiling at them, did seem not to disprove them. So that hereby you may right well perceive how little the courtiers would regard and esteem me and my sayings.'

'I ensure you, Master Raphael' (quoth I), 'I took great delectation in hearing you; all things that you said were spoken so wittily and so pleasantly. And methought myself to be in the meantime not only at home in my country, but also, through the pleasant remembrance of the cardinal, in whose house I was brought up of a child, to wax a child again. And, friend Raphael, though I did bear very great love towards you before, yet seeing you do so earnestly favor this man, you will not believe how much my love towards you is now increased. But yet, all this notwithstanding, I can by no means change my mind, but that I must needs believe that you, if you be disposed and can find in your heart to follow some prince's court, shall with your good counsels greatly help and further the commonwealth. Wherefore there is nothing more appertaining to your duty; that is to say, to the duty of a good man. For whereas your Plato judgeth that weal publics shall by this means attain perfect felicity, either if philosophers be kings, or else if kings give themselves to the study of philosophy; how far, I pray you, shall commonwealths then be from this felicity, if philosophers will [not] vouchsafe to instruct kings with their good counsel?'

'They be not so unkind' (quoth he), 'but they would gladly do it; yea, many have done it already in books that they have put forth, if kings and princes would be willing and ready to follow good counsel. But Plato doubtless did well foresee, unless kings themselves would apply their minds to the study of philosophy, that else they would never thoroughly allow the counsel of philosophers; being themselves before even from their tender age infected and corrupt with perverse and evil opinions. Which thing Plato himself proved true in King Dionysius. If I should propose to any king wholesome decrees, doing my endeavor to pluck out of his mind the pernicious original causes of vice and naughtiness, think you not that I should forthwith either be driven away, or else made a laughing stock?

'Go to, suppose that I were with the French king, and there sitting in his council, whiles that in that most secret consultation, the king himself there being present in his

own person, they beat their brains and search the very
bottoms of their wits to discuss by what craft and means
the king may still keep Milan and draw to him again fugitive Naples; and then how to conquer the Venetians,
and how to bring under his jurisdiction all Italy; then
how to win the dominion of Flanders, Brabant, and of
all Burgundy, with divers other lands, whose kingdoms
he hath long ago in mind and purpose invaded. Here,
whiles one counselleth to conclude a league of peace
with the Venetians, which shall so long endure as shall
be thought meet and expedient for their purpose, and to
make them also of their counsel, yea, and besides that to
give them part of the prey, which afterward, when they
have brought their purpose about after their own minds
they may require and claim again. Another thinketh
best to hire the Germans. Another would have the favor
of the Swychers won with money. Another's advice is *Swychers = Swiss*
to appease the puissant power of the Emperor's majesty
with gold, as with a most pleasant and acceptable sacrifice; whiles another giveth counsel to make peace with
the King of Aragon, and to restore unto him his own
kingdom of Navarre as a full assurance of peace. Another cometh in with his five eggs, and adviseth to hook
in the King of Castile with some hope of affinity or alliance, and to bring to their part certain peers of his court
for great pensions; whiles they all stay at the chiefest
doubt of all, what to do in the meantime with England,
and yet agree all in this to make peace with the Englishmen, and with most sure and strong bonds to bind that
weak and feeble friendship, so that they must be called
friends and had in suspicion as enemies; and that therefore the Scots must be had in a readiness, as it were in a *in aunters =*
standing ready at all occasions, in aunters the English- *in case*

men should stir never so little, incontinent to set upon them; and moreover privily and secretly, for openly it may not be done by the truce that is taken; privily therefore, I say, to make much some peer of England that is banished his country, which must claim title to the crown of the realm, and affirm himself just inheritor thereof; that by this subtle means they may hold to them the king, in whom else they have but small trust and affiance.

'Here, I say, where so great and high matters be in consultation, where so many noble and wise men counsel their king only to war; here, if I, silly man, should rise up and will them to turn over the leaf, and learn a new lesson, saying that my counsel is not to meddle with Italy, but to tarry still at home, and that the kingdom of France alone is almost greater than that it may well be governed of one man; so that the king should not need to study how to get more; and then should propose unto them the decrees of the people that be called the Achoriens, which be situated over against the island of Utopia on the southeast side. These Achoriens once made war in their king's quarrel, for to get him another kingdom which he laid claim unto, and advanced himself right inheritor to the crown thereof, by the title of an old alliance. At the last, when they had gotten it and saw that they had even as much vexation and trouble in keeping it as they had in getting it; and that either their new conquered subjects by sundry occasions were making daily insurrections to rebel against them, or else that other countries were continually with divers inroads and foragings invading them, so that they were ever fighting either for them, or against them, and never could break up their camps; seeing themselves in the

Achoriens; from α–χώρα = those without a place

Utopia; from οὐ–τόπος = no place

mean season pilled and impoverished, their money car- *pilled = plundered*
ried out of the realm, their own men killed to maintain
the glory of another nation, when they had no war, peace
nothing better than war, by reason that their people in
war had inured themselves to corrupt and wicked manners, that they had taken a delight and pleasure in robbing and stealing, that through manslaughter they had
gathered boldness to mischief, that their laws were had
in contempt, and nothing set by or regarded, that their
king, being troubled with the charge and governance of
two kingdoms, could not nor was not able perfectly to
discharge his office towards them both; seeing again that
all these evils and troubles were endless, at the last laid
their heads together and, like faithful and loving subjects, gave to their king free choice and liberty to keep
still the one of these two kingdoms, whether he would;
alleging that he was not able to keep both, and that they
were more than might well be governed of half a king,
forasmuch as no man would be content to take him for
his muleteer that keepeth another man's mules besides
his. So this good prince was constrained to be content
with his old kingdom, and to give over the new to one
of his friends, which shortly after was violently driven
out. Furthermore if I should declare unto them, that all
this busy preparance to war, whereby so many nations
for his sake should be brought into a troublesome hurly-
burly, when all his coffers were emptied, his treasures
wasted and his people destroyed, should at the length
through some mischance be in vain and to none effect;
and that therefore it were best for him to content himself with his own kingdom of France as his forefathers
and predecessors did before him; to make much of it, to
enrich it, and to make it as flourishing as he could; to en-

deavor himself to love his subjects, and again to be beloved of them; willingly to live with them, peaceably to
govern them, and with other kingdoms not to meddle,
seeing that which he hath already is even enough for
him, yea, and more than he can well turn him to; this
mine advice, Master More, how think you it would be
heard and taken?'

'So God help me, not very thankfully,' (quoth I).

'Well, let us proceed then,' (quoth he). 'Suppose that
some king and his council were together whetting their
wits, and devising what subtle craft they might invent to
enrich the king with great treasures of money. First one
counselleth to raise and enhance the valuation of money
when the king must pay any; and again to call down the
value of coin to less than it is worth when he must receive or gather any; for thus great sums shall be paid
with a little money, and where little is due much shall be
received. Another counselleth to feign war, that when
under this color and pretence the king hath gathered
great abundance of money, he may, when it shall please
him, make peace with great solemnity and holy ceremonies, to blind the eyes of the poor commonalty, as taking
pity and compassion, God wot, upon man's blood, like
a loving and a merciful prince.

'Another putteth the king in remembrance of certain
old and moth-eaten laws, that of long time have not been
put in execution; which, because no man can remember
that they were made, every man hath transgressed. The
fines of these laws he counselleth the king to require; for
there is no way so profitable, nor more honorable, as the
which hath a show and color of justice. Another adviseth him to forbid many things under great penalties and
fines, specially such things as is for the people's profit

not be used; and afterward to dispense for money with them, which by this prohibition sustain loss and damage. For by this means the favor of the people is won, and profit riseth two ways: first by taking forfeits of them whom covetousness of gains hath brought in danger of this statute; and also by selling privileges and licenses; which the better that the prince is forsooth, the dearer he selleth them; as one that is loath to grant to any private person anything that is against the profit of his people; and therefore may sell none but at an exceeding dear price.

'Another giveth the king counsel to endanger unto his Grace the judges of the realm, that he may have them ever on his side; which must in every matter dispute and reason for the king's right. And they must be called into the king's palace, and be desired to argue and discuss his matters in his own presence. So there shall be no matter of his, so openly wrong and unjust, wherein one or other of them, either because he will have something to allege and object, or that he is ashamed to say that which is said already, or else to pick a thank with his prince, will not *pick a thank = toady* find some hole open to set a snare in, wherewith to take the contrary part in a trip. Thus whiles the judges can- *trip = offence* not agree among themselves, reasoning and arguing of that which is plain enough, and bringing the manifest truth in doubt, in the mean season the king may take a fit occasion to understand the law as shall most make for his advantage; whereunto all other for shame or for fear will agree. Then the judges may be bold to pronounce of the king's side. For he that giveth sentence for the king cannot be without a good excuse. For it shall be suffi- cient for him to have equity of his part, or the bare words of the law, or a writhen and wrested understanding of the same, or else, which with good and just judges is of greater force than all laws be, the king's indisputable prerogative. To conclude, all the counsellors agree and consent together with the rich Crassus, that no abundance of gold can be sufficient for a prince, which must keep and maintain an army; furthermore that a king, though he would, can do nothing unjustly; for all that all men have, yea also the men themselves, be all his; and that every man hath so much of his own as the king's gentleness hath not taken from him; and that it shall be most for the king's advantage that his subjects have very little or nothing in their possession; as whose safeguard doth herein consist, that his people do not wax wanton and wealthy through riches and liberty, because where these things be, there men be not wont patiently to obey hard, unjust, and unlawful commandments; whereas, on the other part, need and poverty doth hold down and keep under stout courages, and maketh them patient perforce, taking from them bold and rebelling stomachs.

'Here again if I should rise up and boldly affirm that all these counsels be to the king dishonor and reproach, whose honor and safety is more and rather supported and upholden by the wealth and riches of his people than by his own treasures; and if I should declare that the commonalty chooseth their king for their own sake and not for his sake; for this intent that through his labor and study they might all live wealthily, safe from wrongs and injuries; and that therefore the king ought to take more care for the wealth of his people than for his own wealth, even as the office and duty of a shepherd is, in that he is a shepherd, to feed his sheep rather than himself. For as touching this, that they think the defence and maintenance of peace to consist in the poverty of the people, the thing itself showeth that they be far out of the way. For where shall a man find more wrangling, quarrelling, brawling, and chiding, than among beggars? Who be more desirous of new mutations and alterations than they that be not content with the present state of their life? Or, finally, who be bolder stomached to bring all in hurly-burly (thereby trusting to get some windfall), than they that have now nothing to lose? And if so be that there were any king that were so smally regarded, or so behated of his subjects, that other ways he could not keep them in awe but only by open wrongs, by polling and shaving, and by bringing them to beggary; surely it were better for him to forsake his kingdom than to hold it by this means; whereby, though the name of a king be kept, yet the majesty is lost. For it is against the dignity of a king to have rule over beggars, but rather over rich and wealthy men. Of this mind was the hardy and courageous Fabrice, when he said that he had rather be a ruler of rich men that be rich himself. And verily one man to live in pleasure and wealth, whiles all other weep and smart for it, that is the part not of a king but of a jailer.

'To be short, as he is a foolish physician that cannot cure his patient's disease unless he cast him in another sickness; so he that cannot amend the lives of his subjects but by taking from them the wealth and commodity of life, he must needs grant that he knoweth not the feat how to govern free men. But let him rather amend his own life, renounce unhonest pleasures, and forsake pride. For these be the chief vices that cause him to run in the contempt or hatred of his people. Let him live of his own, hurting no man. Let him do cost not above his power. Let him restrain wickedness. Let him prevent *do cost = make expenditures* vices and take away the occasions of offences by well ordering his subjects, and not by suffering wickedness to increase, afterward to be punished. Let him not be too hasty in calling again laws which a custom hath abrogated; specially such as have been long forgotten and never lacked nor needed. And let him never under the cloak and pretence of transgression take such fines and forfeits as no judge will suffer a private person to take, as unjust and full of guile.

'Here if I should bring forth before them the law of the Macarians, which be not far distant from Utopia, whose king, the day of his coronation, is bound by a solemn oath that he shall never at any time have in his treasure above a thousand pound of gold or silver—They say a very good king, which took more care for the wealth and commodity of his country than for the enriching of himself, made this law to be a stop and a bar to kings for heaping and hoarding up so much money as might impoverish their people. For he foresaw that this sum of treasure would suffice to support the king in battle against his own people if they should chance to rebel; and also to maintain his wars against the invasions of his foreign enemies. Again he perceived the same stock of money to be too little and insufficient to encourage and enable him wrongfully to take away other men's goods, which was the chief cause why the law was made. Another cause was this: he thought that by this provision his people should not lack money wherewith to maintain their daily occupying and chaffer. And seeing the king could not choose but lay out and bestow all that came in above the prescript sum of his stock, he thought he would seek no occasions to do his subjects injury. Such a king shall be feared of evil men and loved of good

*Macarians; from
μάχαρες = blessed*

men. These and such other informations if I should use among men wholly inclined and given to the contrary part, how deaf hearers, think you, should I have?'

'Deaf hearers doubtless' (quoth I), 'and in good faith no marvel. And to speak as I think, truly I cannot allow that such communication shall be used, or such counsel given, as you be sure shall never be regarded nor received. For how can so strange informations be profitable, or how can they be beaten into their heads, whose minds be already prevented with clean contrary persuasions? This school philosophy is not unpleasant among friends in familiar communication, but in the councils of kings, where great matters be debated and reasoned with great authority, these things have no place.'

'That is it which I meant' (quoth he), 'when I said philosophy had no place among kings.' 'Indeed,' (quoth I) 'this school philosophy hath not; which thinketh all things meet for every place. But there is another philosophy more civil, which knoweth as ye would say her own stage, and thereafter ordering and behaving herself in the play that she hath in hand, playeth her part accordingly with comeliness, uttering nothing out of due order and fashion. And this is the philosophy that you must use. Or else, whiles a comedy of Plautus is playing, and the vile bondmen scoffing and trifling among themselves, if you should suddenly come upon the stage in a philosopher's apparel, and rehearse out of *Octavia* the place wherein Seneca disputeth with Nero; had it not been better for you to have played the dumb person, than by rehearsing that which served neither for the time nor place to have made such a tragical comedy or gallimaufry? For by bringing in other stuff that nothing appertaineth to the present matter, you must

gallimaufry =
hodgepodge

needs mar and pervert the play that is in hand, though the stuff that you bring be much better. What part soever you have taken upon you, play that as well as you can and make the best of it, and do not therefore disturb and bring out of order the whole matter because that another which is merrier and better cometh to your remembrance.

'So the case standeth in a commonwealth, and so it is in the consultations of kings and princes. If evil opinions and naughty persuasions cannot be utterly and quite plucked out of their hearts, if you cannot even as you would remedy vices, which use and custom hath confirmed, yet for this cause you must not leave and forsake the commonwealth; you must not forsake the ship in a tempest, because you cannot rule and keep down the winds. No, nor you must not labor to drive into their heads new and strange informations which you know well shall be nothing regarded with them that be of clean contrary minds. But you must with a crafty wile and a subtle train study and endeavor yourself, as much as in you lieth, to handle the matter wittily and handsomely for the purpose; and that which you cannot turn to good, so to order it that it be not very bad. For it is not possible for all things to be well, unless all men were good; which I think will not be yet this good many years.'

'By this means' (quoth he) 'nothing else will be brought to pass but, whiles that I go about to remedy the madness of others, I should be even as mad as they. For if I would speak things that be true I must needs speak such things. But as for to speak false things, whether that be a philosopher's part or no I cannot tell; truly it is not my part. Howbeit this communication of mine, though peradventure it may seem unpleasant to them, yet can I not see why it should seem strange or foolishly newfangled. If so be that I should speak those things that Plato feigneth in his weal public, or that the Utopians do in theirs, these things though they were (as they be indeed) better, yet they might seem spoken out of place; forasmuch as here among us, every man hath his possessions several to himself, and there all things be common.

'But what was in my communication contained that might not and ought not in any place to be spoken? saving that to them which have thoroughly decreed and determined with themselves to run headlong the contrary way, it cannot be acceptable and pleasant; because it calleth them back and showeth them the jeopardies. Verily if all things that evil and vicious manners have caused to seem inconvenient and naught should be refused as things unmeet and reproachful, then we must among Christian people wink at the most part of all those things which Christ taught us, and so straitly forbade them to be winked at that those things also which he whispered in the ears of his disciples he commanded to be proclaimed in open houses. And yet the most part of them is more dissident from the manners of the world nowadays than my communication was. But preachers, sly and wily men, following your counsel (as I suppose), because they saw men evil willing to frame their manners to Christ's rule, they have wrested and wried his doctrine, and like a rule of lead have applied it to men's manners, that by some means at the least way they might agree together. Whereby I cannot see what good they have done, but that men may more sickerly be evil. And I truly should prevail even as much in king's councils. For either I must say other ways than they say, and then I were as good to say nothing; or else I must say the same that they say, and (as Mitio saith in Terence) help to further their madness. For that crafty wile and subtle train of yours, I cannot perceive to what purpose it serveth; wherewith you would have me to study and endeavor myself, if all things cannot be made good, yet to handle them wittily and handsomely for the purpose; that, as far forth as is possible they may not be very evil. For there is no place to dissemble in nor to wink in. Naughty counsels must be openly allowed and very pestilent decrees must be approved. He shall be counted worse than a spy, yea almost as evil as a traitor, that with a faint heart doth praise evil and noisome decrees.

'Moreover a man can have no occasion to do good, chancing into the company of them which will sooner make naught a good man, than be made good themselves; through whose evil company he shall be marred, or else if he remain good and innocent, yet the wickedness and foolishness of others shall be imputed to him, and laid in his neck. So that it is impossible with that crafty wile and subtle train to turn anything to better.

'Wherefore Plato by a goodly similitude declareth why wise men refrain to meddle in the commonwealth. For when they see the people swarm into the streets, and daily wet to the skin with rain, and yet cannot persuade them to go out of the rain and to take their houses; knowing well that if they should go out to them they should nothing prevail, nor win aught by it but be wet also in the rain; they do keep themselves within their houses, being content that they be safe themselves, seeing that they cannot remedy the folly of the people.

'Howbeit, doubtless, Master More (to speak truly as my mind giveth me), wheresoever possessions be private, where money beareth all the stroke, it is hard and almost impossible that there the weal public may justly be governed and prosperously flourish. Unless you think thus: that justice is there executed where all things come into the hands of evil men; or that prosperity there flourisheth where all is divided among a few; which few nevertheless do not lead their lives very wealthily, and the residue live miserably, wretchedly, and beggarly.

'Wherefore when I consider with myself, and weigh in my mind the wise and godly ordinances of the Utopians, among whom with very few laws all things be so well and wealthily ordered that virtue is had in price and estimation; and yet, all things being there common every man hath abundance of everything; again, on the other part, when I compare with them so many nations ever making new laws, yet none of them all well and sufficiently furnished with laws; where every man calleth that he hath gotten his own proper and private goods; where so many new laws daily made be not sufficient for every man to enjoy, defend, and know from another man's that which he calleth his own; which thing the infinite controversies in the law, that daily rise never to be ended, plainly declare to be true; these things (I say) when I consider with myself, I hold well with Plato, and do nothing marvel that he would make no laws for them that refused those laws, whereby all men should have and enjoy equal portions of wealths and commodities. For the wise man did easily foresee that this is the one and only way to the wealth of a commonalty, if equality of all things should be brought in and stablished; which I think is not possible to be observed where every man's goods be proper and peculiar to himself. For where every man under certain titles and pretences draweth and plucketh to himself as much as he can, and so a few divide among themselves all the riches that there is, be there never so much abundance and store, there to the residue is left lack and poverty. And for the most part it chanceth that this latter sort is more worthy to enjoy that state of wealth than the other be; because the rich men be covetous, crafty, and unprofitable; on the other part, the poor be lowly, simple, and by their daily labor more profitable to the commonwealth than to themselves.

'Thus I do fully persuade myself that no equal and just distribution of things can be made, nor that perfect wealth shall ever be among men, unless this propriety be exiled and banished. But so long as it shall continue, so long shall remain among the most and best part of men the heavy and inevitable burden of poverty and wretchedness. Which, as I grant that it may be somewhat eased, so I utterly deny that it can wholly be taken away. For if there were a statute made that no man should possess above a certain measure of ground, and that no man should have in his stock above a prescript and appointed sum of money; if it were by certain laws decreed that neither the king should be of too great power, neither the people too proud and wealthy, and that offices should not be obtained by inordinate suit or by bribes and gifts, that they should neither be bought nor sold, nor that it should be needful for the officers to be at any cost or charge in their offices; for so occasion is given to the officers by fraud and ravin to gather up their money again, and by reason of gifts and bribes the offices be given to rich men, which should rather have been executed of wise men; by such laws, I say, like as sick bodies that be desperate and past cure be wont with continual good cherishing to be kept up, so these evils also might be lightened and mitigated. But that they may be perfectly cured and brought to a good and upright state, it is not to be hoped for whiles every man is master of his own to himself. Yea, and whiles you go about to do your cure of one part, you shall make bigger the sore of another part; so the help of one causeth another's harm, forasmuch as nothing can be given to any man, unless that be taken from another.'

'But I am of a contrary opinion' (quoth I) 'for methinketh that men shall never there live wealthily where all things be common. For how can there be abundance of goods, or of anything, where every man withdraweth his hand from labor? whom the regard of his own gains driveth not to work, and the hope that he hath in other men's travails maketh him slothful. Then when they be pricked with poverty, and yet no man can by any law or right defend that for his own which he hath gotten with the labor of his own hands, shall not there of necessity be continual sedition and bloodshed? Specially the authority and reverend of magistrates being taken away; which what place it may have with such men, among whom is no difference, I cannot devise.'

'I marvel not' (quoth he) 'that you be of this opinion. For you conceive in your mind either none at all or else a very false image and similitude of this thing. But if you had been with me in Utopia and had presently seen their fashions and laws as I did, which lived there five years and more and would never have come thence but only to make that new land known here;

then doubtless you would grant that you never saw people well ordered but only there.'

'Surely,' (quoth Master Peter) 'it shall be hard for you to make me believe that there is better order in that new land than is here in these countries that we know. For good wits be as well here as there; and I think our commonwealths be ancienter than theirs, wherein long use and experience hath found out many things commodious for man's life, besides that many things here among us have been found by chance, which no wit could ever have devised.'

'As touching the ancientness' (quoth he) 'of commonwealths, then you might better judge if you had read the histories and chronicles of that land; which if we may believe, cities were there before there were men here. Now what thing soever hitherto by wit hath been devised or found by chance, that might be as well there as here. But I think verily, though it were so that we did pass them in wit, yet in study and laborsome endeavor they far pass us. For (as their chronicles testify) before our arrival there they never heard anything of us, whom they call the Ultraequinoctials, saving that once about twelve hundred years ago a certain ship was lost by the isle of Utopia which was driven thither by tempest. Certain Romans and Egyptians were cast on land, which after that never went thence.

'Mark now what profit they took of this one occasion through diligence and earnest travail. There was no craft nor science within the empery of Rome whereof any profit could rise, but they either learned it of these strangers or else, of them taking occasion to search for it, found it out. So great profit was it to them that ever any went thither from hence. But if any like chance before this hath brought any man from thence hither, that is as quite out of remembrance as this also perchance in time to come shall be forgotten that ever I was there. And like as they quickly, almost at the first meeting, made their own whatsoever is among us wealthily devised; so I suppose it would be long before we would receive anything that among them is better instituted than among us. And this I suppose is the chief cause why their commonwealths be wiselier governed and do flourish in more wealth than ours, though we neither in wit nor in riches be their inferiors.'

'Therefore, gentle Master Raphael,' (quoth I) 'I pray you and beseech you describe unto us the island. And study not to be short; but declare largely in order their grounds, their rivers, their cities, their people, their manners, their ordinances, their laws, and, to be short, all things that you shall think us desirous to know. And you shall think us desirous to know whatsoever we know not yet.'

'There is nothing' (quoth he) 'that I will do gladlier. For all these things I have fresh in mind. But the matter requireth leisure.'

'Let us go in, therefore' (quoth I) 'to dinner: afterward we will bestow the time at our pleasure.'

'Content' (quoth he) 'be it.'

So we went in and dined. When dinner was done, we came into the same place again and sat us down upon the same bench, commanding our servants that no man should trouble us. Then I and Master Peter Giles desired Master Raphael to perform his promise. He therefore, seeing us desirous and willing to hearken to him, when he had sit still and paused a little while, musing and bethinking himself, thus he began to speak:

The end of the first Book.

THE

SECOND BOOK

of the communication of
Raphael Hythloday
concerning the
best state of a
common-
wealth

Containing the description of
Utopia, with a declaration of
the Godly government
and of all the good
laws and orders
of the same
island.

ℭ

BOOK TWO

HE island of Utopia containeth in breadth in the middle part of it (for there it is broadest) two hundred miles, which breadth continueth through the most part of the land, saving that by little and little it cometh in and waxeth narrower towards both the ends; which, fetching about a circuit or compass of five hundred miles, do fashion the whole island like to the new moon. Between those two corners the sea runneth in, dividing them asunder by the distance of eleven miles or thereabouts, and there surmounteth into a large and wide sea, which, by reason that the land of every side compasseth it about and sheltereth it from the winds, is not rough nor mounteth not with great waves, but almost floweth quietly, not much unlike a great standing pool, and maketh almost all the space, within the belly of the land in manner of a haven, and to the great commodity of the inhabitants receiveth in ships towards every part of the land. The forefronts or frontiers of the two corners, what with fords and shelves and what with rocks, be very jeopardous and dangerous. In the middle distance between them both standeth up above the water a great rock, which therefore is nothing perilous because it is in sight. Upon the top of this rock is a fair and a strong tower builded, which they hold with a garrison of men. Other rocks there be that lie hid under the water and therefore be dangerous. The channels be known only to themselves and therefore it seldom chanceth that any stranger, unless he be guided by a Utopian, can come into this haven, insomuch that they themselves could scarcely enter without jeopardy but that their way is directed and ruled by certain landmarks standing on the shore. By turning, translating and removing these marks into other places they may destroy their enemies' navies, be they never so many. The outside of the land is also full of havens, but the landing is so surely defenced, what by nature and what by workmanship of man's hand, that a few defenders may drive back many armies.

Howbeit, as they say, and as the fashion of the place itself doth partly show, it was not ever compassed about with the sea. But King Utopus, whose name as conqueror the island beareth (for before that time it was called Abraxa), which also brought the rude and wild people to that excellent perfection in all good fashions, humanity, and civil gentleness wherein they now go beyond all the people of the world; even at his first arriving and entering upon the land, forthwith obtaining the victory caused fifteen miles space of uplandish ground where the sea had no passage, to be cut and digged up, and so brought the sea round about the land. He set to this work not only the inhabitants of the island (because they should not think it done in contumely and despite), but also all his own soldiers. Thus the work, being divided into so great a number of workmen, was with exceeding marvelous speed despatched;

insomuch that the borderers, which at the first began to mock and to jest at this vain enterprise, then turned their laughter to marvel at the success, and to fear.

There be in the island fifty-four large and fair cities or shire-towns, agreeing all together in one tongue, in like manners, institutions, and laws. They be all set and situate alike and in all points fashioned alike, as far forth as the place or plot suffereth. Of these cities they that be nighest together be twenty-four miles asunder. Again there is none of them distant from the next above one day's journey afoot.

There come yearly to Amaurote out of every city three old men, wise and well experienced, there to entreat and debate of the common matters of the land. For this city (because it standeth just in the midst of the island and is therefore most meet for the ambassadors of all parts of the realm) is taken for the chief and head city. The precincts and bounds of the shires be so commodiously appointed out and set forth for the cities that never a one of them all hath of any side less than twenty miles of ground, and of some side also much more, as of that part where the cities be of farther distance asunder. None of the cities desire to enlarge the bounds and limits of their shires, for they count themselves rather the good husbands than the owners of their lands.

Amaurote; from
ἀμαυϱός = obscure

They have in the country, in all parts of the shire, houses or farms builded, well appointed and furnished with all sorts of instruments and tools belonging to husbandry. These houses be inhabited of the citizens which come thither to dwell by course. No household or farm in the country hath fewer than forty persons, men and women, besides two bondmen, which be all under the rule and order of the good man and the good wife of the house, being both very sage and discreet persons. And every thirty farms or families have one head ruler which is called a phylarch, being as it were a head bailiff. Out of every one of these families or farms cometh every year into the city twenty persons which have continued two years before in the country. In their place so many fresh be sent thither out of the city, which of them that have been there a year already and be therefore expert and cunning in husbandry, shall be instructed and taught; and they the next year shall teach other. This order is used, for fear that either scarceness of victuals or some other like incommodity should chance through lack of knowledge if they should be all together new and fresh and unexpert in husbandry. This manner and fashion of yearly changing and renewing the occupiers of husbandry, though it be solemn and customably used to the intent that no man shall be constrained against his will to continue long in that hard and sharp kind of life, yet many of them have such a pleasure and delight in husbandry that they obtain a longer space of years. These husbandmen plow and till the ground, and breed up cattle, and make ready wood, which they carry to the city either by land or by water, as they may most conveniently. They bring up a great multitude of pullen, and that by a marvelous policy. For the hens do not sit upon the eggs; but by keeping them in a certain equal heat they bring life into them and hatch them. The chickens, as soon as they be come out of the shell, follow men and women instead of the hens.

They bring up very few horses, nor none but very fierce ones, and for none other use or purpose but only

phylarch; from
ψύλαρχος =
tribal chief

to exercise their youth in riding and feats of arms. For oxen be put to all the labor of plowing and drawing, which they grant to be not so good as horses at a sudden brunt and (as we say) at a dead lift; but yet they hold opinion that they will abide and suffer much more labor and pain than horses will. And they think that they be not in danger and subject unto so many diseases, and that they be kept and maintained with much less cost and charge, and finally that they be good for meat when they be past labor.

They sow corn only for bread, for their drink is either wine made of grapes, or else of apples or pears, or else it is clean water; and many times meath made of honey or licorice sodden in water, for thereof they have *meath = mead* great store. And though they know certainly (for they know it perfectly indeed), how much victuals the city with the whole country or shire round about it doth spend, yet they sow much more corn and breed up much more cattle than serveth for their own use, and the overplus they part among their borderers. Whatsoever necessary things be lacking in the country, all such stuff they fetch out of the city, where, without any exchange, they easily obtain it of the magistrates of the city. For every month many of them go into the city on the holy day. When their harvest day draweth near and is at hand, then the phylarchs, which be the head officers and bailiffs of husbandry, send word to the magistrates of the city what number of harvest-men is needful to be sent to them out of the city, the which company of harvest-men, being there ready at the day appointed, almost in one fair day despatcheth all the harvest work.

Of the Cities and namely of Amaurote.

As for their cities, he that knoweth one of them knoweth them all; they be all so like one to another, as far
forth as the nature of the place permitteth. I will describe therefore to you one or other of them, for it
skilleth = matters   skilleth not greatly which; but which rather than Amaurote? Of them all this is the worthiest and of most
dignity, for the residue knowledge it for the head city
because there is the council house. Nor to me any of
them all is better beloved, as wherein I lived five whole
years together.

The city of Amaurote standeth upon the side of a
low hill, in fashion almost foursquare; for the breadth
of it beginneth a little beneath the top of the hill, and
still continueth by the space of two miles until it come
to the river of Anyder; the length of it which lieth by
the river's side is somewhat more.

Anyder; from   The river of Anyder riseth twenty-four miles above
ἄνυδρος =   Amaurote out of a little spring, but being increased by
waterless   other small floods and brooks that run into it, and
among others two somewhat big ones, before the city
it is half a mile broad, and farther broader, and sixty
miles beyond the city it falleth into the ocean sea. By
all that space that lieth between the sea and the city, and
a good sort of miles also above the city, the water ebbeth and floweth six hours together with a swift tide.
When the sea floweth in for the length of thirty miles
it filleth all the Anyder with salt water and driveth back
the fresh water of the river, and somewhat further it
changeth the sweetness of the fresh water with saltness.
But a little beyond that the river waxeth sweet, and run-

neth forby the city fresh and pleasant; and when the sea ebbeth and goeth back again the fresh water followeth it almost even to the very fall into the sea.

There goeth a bridge over the river, made not of piles or of timber, but of stonework with gorgeous and substantial arches, at that part of the city that is farthest from the sea; to the intent that ships may go along forby all the side of the city without let. They have also another river which indeed is not very great, but it runneth gently and pleasantly, for it riseth even out of the same hill that the city standeth upon and runneth down a slope through the midst of the city into Anyder. And because it riseth a little without the city, the Amaurotians have enclosed the headspring of it with strong fences and bulwarks and so have joined it to the city. This is done to the intent that the water should not be stopped nor turned away or poisoned if their enemies should chance to come upon them. From thence the water is derived and brought down in canals of brick divers ways into the lower parts of the city. Where that cannot be done, by reason that the place will not suffer it, there they gather the rainwater in great cisterns, which doth them as good service.

The city is compassed about with a high and thick wall, full of turrets and bulwarks. A dry ditch, but deep and broad and overgrown with bushes, briars, and thorns, goeth about three sides or quarters of the city; to the fourth side the river itself serveth for a ditch. The streets be appointed and set forth very commodious and handsome, both for carriage and also against the winds. The houses be of fair and gorgeous building, and in the street side they stand joined together in a long row through the whole street without any partition or separation. The streets be twenty foot broad. On the back side of the houses, through the whole length of the street, lie large gardens which be closed in round about with the back part of the streets. Every house hath two doors, one into the street and a postern-door on the back side into the garden. These doors be made with two leaves, never locked nor bolted, so easy to be opened that they will follow the least drawing of a finger and shut again by themselves. Every man that will may go in, for there is nothing within the houses that is private or any man's own. And every ten year they change their houses by lot.

They set great store by their gardens. In them they have vineyards, all manner of fruit, herbs, and flowers, so pleasant, so well furnished, and so finely kept, that I never saw thing more fruitful nor better trimmed in any place. Their study and diligence herein cometh not only of pleasure, but also of a certain strife and contention that is between street and street, concerning the trimming, husbanding, and furnishing of their gardens, every man for his own part. And verily you shall not lightly find in all the city anything that is more commodious, either for the profit of the citizens or for pleasure. And therefore it may seem that the first founder of the city minded nothing so much as he did these gardens.

For they say that King Utopus himself, even at the first beginning, appointed and drew forth the platform of the city into this fashion and figure that it hath now; but the gallant garnishing, and the beautiful setting forth of it, whereunto he saw that one man's age would not suffice, that he left to his posterity. For their chronicles, which they keep written with all diligent circumspection, containing the history of seventeen hundred and sixty years, even from the first conquest of the island, record and witness that the houses in the beginning were very low, and like homely cottages or poor shepherd-houses, made at all adventures of every rude piece of wood that came first to hands, with mud walls and ridged roofs thatched over with straw. But now the houses be curiously builded, after a gorgeous and gallant sort, with three stories one over another. The outsides of the walls be made either of hard flint or of plaster or else of brick, and the inner sides be well strengthened with timber-work. The roofs be plain and flat, covered with a certain kind of plaster that is of no cost and yet so tempered that no fire can hurt or perish it, and withstandeth the violence of the weather better than any lead. They keep the wind out of their windows with glass, for it is there much used; and somewhere also with fine linen cloth dipped in oil or amber, and that for two commodities, for by this means more light cometh in and the wind is better kept out.

Of the Magistrates.

Every thirty families or farms choose them yearly an officer, which in their old language is called the syphogrant, and by a newer name the phylarch. Every ten syphogrants, with all their three hundred families, be under an officer which was once called the tranibore, now the chief phylarch.

Moreover, as concerning the election of the prince, all the syphogrants, which be in number two hundred, first be sworn to choose him whom they think most meet and expedient. Then by a secret election they name

prince one of those four whom the people before named
unto them; for out of the four quarters of the city there
be four chosen, out of every quarter one, to stand for
the election, which be put up to the council. The prince's
office continueth all his lifetime unless he be deposed
or put down for suspicion of tyranny. They choose
the tranibores yearly, but lightly they change them not.
All the other offices be but for one year. The tranibores
every third day, and sometimes, if need be, oftener,
come into the council-house with the prince. Their
council is concerning the commonwealth. If there be
any controversies among the commoners, which be very
few, they despatch and end them by and by. They take
ever two syphogrants to them in counsel, and every day
a new couple. And that is provided that nothing touching the commonwealth shall be confirmed and ratified
unless it have been reasoned of and debated three days
in the council before it be decreed. It is death to have
any consultation for the commonwealth out of the council or the place of the common election. This statute,
they say, was made to the intent that the prince and
tranibores might not easily conspire together to oppress
the people by tyranny and to change the state of the
weal public. Therefore matters of great weight and importance be brought to the election-house of the syphogrants, which open the matter to their families; and
afterward, when they have consulted among themselves,
they show their device to the council. Sometime the
matter is brought before the council of the whole island.

Furthermore, this custom also the council useth, to
dispute or reason of no matter the same day that it is first
proposed or put forth, but to defer it to the next sitting
of the council; because that no man when he hath rashly

there spoken that cometh first to his tongue's end shall then afterward rather study for reasons wherewith to defend and confirm his first foolish sentence than for the commodity of the commonwealth; as one rather willing the harm or hindrance of the weal public than any loss or diminution of his own existimation; and as one that would not for shame (which is a very foolish shame) be counted anything overseen in the matter at the first, who at the first ought to have spoken rather wisely than hastily or rashly.

existimation = reputation

Of Sciences, Crafts and Occupations.

HUSBANDRY is a science common to them all in general, both men and women, wherein they be all expert and cunning. In this they be all instruct even from their youth; partly in schools with traditions and precepts, and partly in the country nigh the city, brought up as it were in playing, not only beholding the use of it but by occasion of exercising their bodies practising it also.

Besides husbandry, which (as I said) is common to them all, every one of them learneth one or other several and particular science as his own proper craft. That is most commonly either clothworking in wool or flax, or masonry, or the smith's craft, or the carpenter's science; for there is none other occupation that any number to speak of doth use there. For their garments, which throughout all the island be of one fashion (saving that there is a difference between the man's garment and the woman's, between the married and the unmarried), and this one continueth forevermore unchanged, seemly and comely to the eye, no let to the moving and wielding of the body, also fit both for winter and summer; as for these garments (I say) every family maketh their own. But of the other foresaid crafts every man learneth one, and not only the men but also the women. But the women, as the weaker sort, be put to the easier crafts; they work wool and flax. The other more laborsome sciences be committed to the men. For the most part every man is brought up in his father's craft, for most commonly they be naturally thereto bent and inclined. But if a man's mind stand to any other, he is by adoption put into a family of that occupation which he doth most fantasy; whom not only his father, but also the magistrates do diligently look to that he be put to a discreet and an honest householder. Yea, and if any person, when he hath learned one craft, be desirous to learn also another, he is likewise suffered and permitted. When he hath learned both, he occupieth whether he will, unless the city have more need of the one than of the other.

The chief and almost the only office of the syphogrants is to see and take heed that no man sit idle, but that every one apply his own craft with earnest diligence, and yet for all that not to be wearied from early in the morning to late in the evening with continual work, like laboring and toiling beasts. For this is worse than the miserable and wretched condition of bondmen, which nevertheless is almost everywhere the life of workmen and artificers, saving in Utopia. For they, dividing the day and the night into twenty-four just hours, appoint and assign only six of those hours to work; three before noon, upon the which they go straight to dinner, and after dinner, when they have rested two hours, then they work three; and upon that they go to supper. About eight of the clock in the evening (counting one of the clock at the first hour after noon) they

go to bed. Eight hours they give to sleep. All the void
time, that is, between the hours of work, sleep, and meat,
that they be suffered to bestow, every man as he liketh
best himself; not to the intent they should misspend this
time in riot or slothfulness, but, being then licensed from
the labor of their own occupations, to bestow the time
well and thriftily upon some other good science, as shall
please them. For it is a solemn custom there to have
lectures daily early in the morning, where to be present
they only be constrained that be namely chosen and
appointed to learning. Howbeit a great multitude of
every sort of people, both men and women, go to hear
lectures; some one and some another, as every man's
nature is inclined. Yet this notwithstanding, if any man
had rather bestow this time upon his own occupation (as
it chanceth in many whose minds rise not in the contemplation of any science liberal) he is not letted nor
prohibited but is also praised and commended, as profitable to the commonwealth.

After supper they bestow one hour in play, in summer in their gardens, in winter in their common halls,
where they dine and sup. There they exercise themselves in music, or else in honest and wholesome communication. Dice play and such other foolish and pernicious games they know not, but they use two games
not much unlike the chess. The one is the battle of num-
bers, wherein one number stealeth away another. The
other is wherein vices fight with virtues, as it were in
battle array, or a set field; in the which game is very
properly showed both the strife and discord that vices
have among themselves, and again their unity and concord against virtues; and also what vices be repugnant
to what virtues, with what power and strength they as-

sail them openly, by what wiles and subtlety they assault them secretly, with what help and aid the virtues resist and overcome the puissance of the vices, by what craft they frustrate their purposes, and finally, by what sleight of means the one getteth the victory.

But here, lest you be deceived, one thing you must look more narrowly upon. For seeing they bestow but six hours in work, perchance you may think that the lack of some necessary things hereof may ensue. But this is nothing so; for that small time is not only enough but also too much for the store and abundance of all things that be requisite either for the necessity or commodity of life, the which thing you also shall perceive if you weigh and consider with yourselves how great a part of the people in other countries liveth idle; first, almost all women, which be the half of the whole number, or else, if the women be anywhere occupied, there most commonly in their stead the men be idle. Besides this, how great and how idle a company is there of priests and religious men, as they call them? Put thereto all rich men, specially all landed men, which commonly be called gentlemen and noblemen. Take into this number also their servants; I mean all that flock of stout, bragging rush-bucklers. Join to them also sturdy and valiant beggars cloaking their idle life under the color of some disease or sickness, and truly you shall find them much fewer than you thought by whose labor all these things be gotten that men use and live by. Now consider with yourself, of these few that do work, how few be occupied in necessary works, for where money beareth all the swing, there many vain and superfluous occupations must needs be used to serve only for riotous superfluity and unhonest pleasure. For the same multitude that now is occupied in work, if they were divided into so few occupations as the necessary use of nature requireth, in so great plenty of things as then of necessity would ensue, doubtless the prices would be too little for the artificers to maintain their livings. But if all these that be now busied about unprofitable occupations, with all the whole flock of them that live idly and slothfully, which consume and waste every one of them more of these things that come by other men's labor than two of the workmen themselves do; if all these (I say) were set to profitable occupations you easily perceive how little time would be enough, yea and too much, to store us with all things that may be requisite either for necessity or for commodity; yea, or for pleasure, so that the same pleasure be true and natural.

And this in Utopia the thing itself maketh manifest and plain; for there in all the city, with the whole country or shire adjoining to it, scarcely five hundred persons of all the whole number of men and women that be neither too old nor too weak to work be licensed from labor. Among them the syphogrants, which (though they be by the laws exempt and privileged from labor) yet they exempt not themselves; to the intent they may the rather by their example provoke other to work. The same vacation from labor do they also enjoy to whom the people, persuaded by the commendation of the priests and secret election of the syphogrants, have given a perpetual license from labor to learning. But if any one of them prove not according to the expectation and hope of him conceived, he is forthwith plucked back to the company of artificers. And contrariwise often it chanceth that a handicraftsman doth so earnestly bestow his vacant and spare hours in learning and through diligence so profit therein, that he is taken from his handy occupation and promoted to the company of the learned.

Out of this order of the learned be chosen ambassadors, priests, tranibores, and finally the prince himself; whom they in their old tongue call Barzanes, and by a newer name, Ademus. The residue of the people being neither idle neither occupied about unprofitable exercises, it may be easily judged in how few hours how much good work by them may be done towards those things that I have spoken of. This commodity they have also above other, that in the most part of necessary occupations they need not so much work as other nations do. For first of all the building or repairing of houses asketh everywhere so many men's continual labor because that the unthrifty heir suffereth the houses that his father builded in continuance of time to fall in decay, so that which he might have upholden with little cost, his successor is constrained to build it again anew, to his great charge. Yea, many times also the house that stood one man in much money, another is of so nice and so delicate a mind that he setteth nothing by it; and it being neglected, and therefore shortly falling into ruin, he buildeth up another in another place with no less cost and charge. But among the Utopians, where all things be set in a good order and the commonwealth in a good stay, it very seldom chanceth that they choose a new plot to build an house upon. And they do not only find speedy and quick remedies for present faults but also prevent them that be like to fall. And by this means their houses continue and last very long with little labor and small reparations, insomuch that this kind of workmen sometimes have almost nothing to do, but that

Ademus; from
α = without,
δῆμος = people

they be commanded to hew timber at home and to square and trim up stones, to the intent that if any work chance, it may the speedier rise.

Now, sir, in their apparel mark, I pray you, how few workmen they need. First of all, whiles they be at work they be covered homely with leather or skins that will last seven years. When they go forth abroad, they cast upon them a cloak which hideth the other homely apparel. These cloaks throughout the whole island be all of one color, and that is the natural color of the wool. They therefore do not only spend much less woolen cloth than is spent in other countries, but also the same standeth them in much less cost. But linen cloth is made with less labor and is therefore had more in use. But in linen cloth only whiteness, in woolen only cleanliness, is regarded. As for the smallness or fineness of the thread, that is nothing passed for, and this is the cause wherefore in other places four or five cloth gowns of divers colors and as many silk coats be not enough for one man. Yea, and if he be of the delicate and nice sort, ten be too few, whereas there one garment will serve a man most commonly two years. For why should he desire more? seeing if he had them, he should not be the better happed or covered from cold, neither in his apparel any whit the comelier.

Wherefore, seeing they be all exercised in profitable occupations and that few artificers in the same crafts be sufficient, this is the cause that, plenty of all things being among them, they do sometimes bring forth an innumerable company of people to amend the highways if any be broken. Many times also, when they have no such work to be occupied about, an open proclamation is made that they shall bestow fewer hours in work. For the magistrates do not exercise their citizens against their wills in unneedful labors. For why? In the institution of that weal public this end is only and chiefly pretended and minded, that what time may possibly be spared from the necessary occupations and affairs of the common-wealth, all that the citizens should withdraw from the bodily service to the free liberty of the mind and garnishing of the same. For herein they suppose the felicity of this life to consist.

Of their living and mutual conversations together.

BUT now will I declare how the citizens use themselves one towards another, what familiar occupying and entertainment there is among the people, and what fashion they use in distributing everything. First, the city consisteth of families: the families most commonly be made of kindreds. For the women, when they be married at a lawful age, they go into their husbands' houses; but the male children, with all the whole male offspring, continue still in their own family and be governed of the eldest and ancientest father, unless he dote for age; for then the next to him in age is put in his room.

But to the intent the prescript number of the citizens should neither decrease nor above measure increase, it is ordained that no family, which in every city be six thousand in the whole, besides them of the country, shall at once have fewer children of the age of fourteen years or thereabout than ten or more than sixteen; for of children under this age no number can be appointed. This measure or number is easily observed and kept by putting them that in fuller families be above the number into families of smaller increase. But if chance be that in the whole city the store increases above the just number, therewith they fill up the lack of other cities. But if so be that the multitude throughout the whole island pass and exceed the due number, then they choose out of every city certain citizens and build up a town under their own laws in the next land where the inhabitants have much waste and unoccupied ground, receiving also of the inhabitants to them, if they will join and dwell with them. They thus joining and dwelling together do easily agree in one fashion of living, and that to the great wealth of both the peoples, for they so bring the matter about by their laws that the ground which before was neither good nor profitable for the one nor for the other, is now sufficient and fruitful enough for them both. But if the inhabitants of that land will not dwell with them to be ordered by their laws, then they drive them out of those bounds which they have limited and appointed out for themselves. And if they resist and rebel, then they make war against them; for they count this the most just cause of war, when any people holdeth a piece of ground void and vacant to no good nor profitable use, keeping other from the use and possession of it which notwithstanding by the law of nature ought thereof to be nourished and relieved. If any chance do so much diminish the number of any of their cities that it cannot be filled up again without the diminishing of the just number of the other cities (which they say chanced but twice since the beginning of the land, through a great pestilent plague) then they make up the number with citizens fetched out of their own foreign towns, for they had rather suffer their foreign towns to decay and perish than any city of their own island to be diminished.

But now again to the conversation of the citizens among themselves. The eldest (as I said) ruleth the family. The wives be ministers to their husbands, the children to their parents, and, to be short, the younger to their elders. Every city is divided into four equal parts. In the midst of every quarter there is a market place of all manner of things; thither the works of every family be brought into certain houses, and every kind of thing is laid up several in barns or storehouses. From hence the father of every family or every householder fetcheth whatsoever he and his have need of, and carrieth it away with him without money, without exchange, without any gage or pledge. For why should anything be denied unto him, seeing there is abundance of all things and that it is not to be feared lest any man will ask more than he needeth? For why should it be thought that that man would ask more than enough which is sure never to lack? Certainly, in all kinds of living creatures, either *ravin = plunder* fear of lack doth cause covetousness and ravin, or in man only pride; which counteth it a glorious thing to pass and excel other in the superfluous and vain ostentation of things, the which kind of vice among the Utopians can have no place.

Next to the market places that I spake of stand meat markets, whither be brought not only all sorts of herbs, and the fruits of trees, with bread, but also fish, and all manner of four-footed beasts and wild fowl that be man's meat. But first the filthiness and ordure thereof is clean washed away in the running river, without the city, in places appointed, meet for the same purpose. From thence the beasts [be] brought in killed and clean washed by the hands of their bondmen; for they permit not their free citizens to accustom their selves to the killing of beasts, through the use whereof they think that clemency, the gentlest affection of our nature, doth by little and little decay and perish. Neither they suffer anything that is filthy, loathsome, or uncleanly to be brought into the city, lest the air, by the stench thereof infected and corrupt, should cause pestilent diseases.

Moreover every street hath certain great large halls set in equal distance one from another, every one known by a several name. In these halls dwell the syphogrants; and to every one of the same halls be appointed thirty families, of either side fifteen. The stewards of every hall at a certain hour come into the meat markets where they receive meat according to the number of their halls.

But first and chiefly of all, respect is had to the sick that be cured in the hospitals. For in the circuit of the city, a little without the walls, they have four hospitals, so big, so wide, so ample, and so large that they may seem four little towns, which were devised of that bigness partly to the intent the sick, be they never so many in number, should not lie too throng or strait and therefore uneasily and incommodiously, and partly that they which were taken and holden with contagious diseases, such as be wont by infection to creep from one to another, might be laid apart far from the company of the residue. These hospitals be so well appointed and with all things necessary to health so furnished, and moreover so diligent attendance through the continual presence of cunning physicians is given that, though no man be sent thither against his will, yet notwithstanding there is no sick person in all the city that had not rather lie there than at home in his own house. When the steward of the sick hath received such meats as the physicians have prescribed, then the best is equally divided among the halls, according to the company of every one, saving that there is had a respect to the prince, the bishop, the tranibores, and to ambassadors and all strangers, if there be any, which be very few and seldom. But they also, when they be there, have certain houses appointed and prepared for them.

To these halls at the set hours of dinner and supper cometh all the whole syphogranty or ward, warned by the noise of a brazen trumpet, except such as be sick in the hospitals or else in their own houses. Howbeit, no man is prohibited or forbid, after the halls be served, to fetch home meat out of the market to his own house, for they know that no man will do it without a cause reasonable. For though no man be prohibited to dine at home, yet no man doth it willingly, because it is counted a point of small honesty, and also it were a folly to take the pain to dress a bad dinner at home when they may be welcome to good and fine fare so nigh hand at the hall. In this hall all vile service, all slavery and drudgery with all laborsome toil and business is done by bondmen. But the women of every family by course have the office and charge of cookery, for seething and dressing the meat and ordering all things thereto belonging. They sit at three tables or more, according to the number of their company. The men sit upon the bench next the wall and the women against them on the other side of the table; that, if any sudden evil should chance to them, as many times happeneth to women with child, they may rise without trouble or disturbance of anybody, and go thence into the nursery.

The nurses sit several alone with their young sucklings in a certain parlor appointed and deputed to the same purpose, never without fire and clean water, nor yet without cradles; that when they will they may lay down the young infants, and at their pleasure take them out of their swathing clothes and hold them to the fire, and refresh them with play. Every mother is nurse to her own child, unless either death or sickness be the let. When that chanceth, the wives of the syphogrants quickly provide a nurse. And that is not hard to be done, for they that can do it do proffer themselves to no service so gladly as to that; because that there this kind of pity is much praised, and the child that is nourished ever after taketh his nurse for his own natural mother. Also among the nurses sit all the children that be under the age of five years. All the other children of both kinds, as well boys as girls, that be under the age of marriage, do either serve at the tables, or else, if they be too young thereto, yet they stand by with marvelous silence. That which is given to them from the table they eat, and other several dinner time they have none. The syphogrant and his wife sitteth in the midst of the high table, forasmuch as that is counted the honorablest place, and because from thence all the whole company is in their sight; for that table standeth overthwart the over end *overthwart the* of the hall. To them be joined two of the ancientest and *over = across the* eldest, for at every table they sit four at a mess. But if *upper* there be a church standing in that syphogranty or ward, then the priest and his wife sitteth with the syphogrant as chief in the company. On both sides of them sit young men, and next unto them again old men; and thus throughout all the house equal of age be set together and yet be mixed with unequal ages. This they say was ordained to the intent that the sage gravity and reverence of the elders should keep the youngers from wanton license of words and behavior; forasmuch as nothing can be so secretly spoken or done at the table but either they that sit on the one side or on the other must needs perceive it. The dishes be not set down in order from the first place, but all the old men (whose places be marked with some special token to be known) be first served of their meat, and then the residue equally. The old men divide their dainties, as they think best, to the younger that sit of both sides them. Thus the elders be not defrauded of their due honor, and nevertheless equal commodity cometh to every one.

They begin every dinner and supper of reading something that pertaineth to good manners and virtue; but it is short, because no man shall be grieved therewith. Hereof the elders take occasion of honest communication, but neither sad nor unpleasant. Howbeit, they do not spend all the whole dinner time themselves with long and tedious talks, but they gladly hear also the young men; yea and do purposely provoke them to talk, to the intent that they may have a proof of every man's wit and towardness or disposition to virtue, which commonly in the liberty of feasting doth show and utter itself. Their dinners be very short, but their suppers be somewhat longer; because that after dinner followeth labor, after supper sleep and natural rest, which they think to be of no more strength and efficacy to wholesome and healthful digestion. No supper is passed without music, nor *banquets = desserts;* their banquets lack no conceits nor junkets. They burn *conceits =* sweet gums and spices for perfumes and pleasant smells, *confectionery;* and sprinkle about sweet ointments and waters; yea they *junkets = delicacies* leave nothing undone that maketh for the cheering of the company. For they be much inclined to this opinion: to think no kind of pleasure forbidden, whereof cometh no harm.

Thus therefore and after this sort they live together in the city; but in the country they that dwell alone, far from any neighbors, do dine and sup at home in their own houses. For no family there lacketh any kind of victuals, as from whom cometh all that the citizens eat and live by.

Of their journeying or traveling abroad, with divers other matters cunningly reasoned and wittily discussed.

But if any be desirous to visit either their friends that dwell in another city or to see the place itself, they easily obtain license of their syphogrants and tranibores, unless there be some profitable let. No man goeth out alone, but a company is sent forth together with their prince's letters, which do testify that they have license to go that journey, and prescribeth also the day of their return. They have a wagon given them, with a common bondman, which driveth the oxen and taketh charge of them. But unless they have women in their company, they send home the wagon again, as an impediment and a let. And though they carry nothing forth with them, yet in all their journey they lack nothing, for wheresoever they come they be at home. If they tarry in a place longer than one day, then there every one of them falleth to his own occupation, and be very gently entertained of the workmen and companies of the same crafts. If any man of his own head and without leave walk out of his precinct and bounds, taken without the prince's letters, he is brought again for a fugitive or a runaway with great shame and rebuke, and is sharply punished.

If he be taken in that fault again he is punished with bondage.

If any be desirous to walk abroad into the fields or into the country that belongeth to the same city that he dwelleth in, obtaining the good-will of his father and the consent of his wife, he is not prohibited. But into what part of the country soever he cometh, he hath no meat given him until he have wrought out his forenoon's task, or else dispatched so much work as there is wont to be wrought before supper. Observing this law and condition, he may go whither he will within the bounds of his own city, for he shall be no less profitable to the city than if he were within it.

Now you see how little liberty they have to loiter, how they can have no cloak or pretence to idleness. There be neither wine-taverns nor ale-houses nor stews nor any occasion of vice or wickedness, no lurking corners, no places of wicked counsels or unlawful assemblies, but they be in the present sight and under the eyes of every man; so that of necessity they must either apply their accustomed labors or else recreate themselves with honest and laudable pastimes.

This fashion being used among the people, they must of necessity have store and plenty of all things; and seeing they be all thereof partners equally, therefore can no man there be poor or needy. In the council of Amaurote (whither, as I said, every city sendeth three men apiece yearly), as soon as it is perfectly known of what things there is in every place plenty, and again what things be scant in any place, incontinent the lack of the one is performed and filled up with the abundance of the other. And this they do freely without any benefit, taking nothing again of them to whom the things is given; but those

incontinent =
immediately

cities that have given of their store to any other city that lacketh, requiring nothing again of the same city, do take such things as they lack of another city, to whom they gave nothing. So the whole island is, as it were, one family or household.

But when they have made sufficient provision of store for themselves (which they think not done until they have provided for two years following, because of the uncertainty of the next year's proof), then of those things whereof they have abundance they carry forth into other countries great plenty; as grain, honey, flax, wool, wood, madder, purple dye, fells, wax, tallow, leather, and living beasts. And the seventh part of all these things they give frankly and freely to the poor of that country; the residue they sell at a reasonable and mean price. By this trade of traffic or merchandise, they bring into their own country not only great plenty of gold and silver but also all such things as they lack at home, which is almost nothing but iron. And by reason they have long used this trade, now they have more abundance of these things than any man will believe. Now, therefore, they care not whether they sell for ready money or else upon trust to be paid at a day and to have the most part in debts. But in so doing they never follow the credence of private men, but the assurance or warrantise of the whole city, by instruments and writings made in that behalf accordingly. When the day of payment is come and expired the city gathereth up the debt of the private debtors and putteth it into the common box, and so long hath the use and profit of it until the Utopians, their creditors, demand it. The most part of it they never ask, for that thing which is to them no profit, to take it from other to whom it is profitable, they

fells = skins

think it no right nor conscience. But if the case so stand that they must lend part of that money to another people, then they require their debt; or when they have war, for the which purpose only they keep at home all the treasure which they have, to be holpen and succored by it either in extreme jeopardies or in sudden dangers, but especially and chiefly to hire therewith, and that for unreasonable great wages, strange soldiers. For they had rather put strangers in jeopardy than their own countrymen, knowing that for money enough their enemies themselves many times may be bought and sold, or else through treason be set together by the ears among themselves. For this cause they keep an inestimable treasure; but yet not as a treasure, but so they have it and use it as in good faith I am ashamed to show, fearing that my words shall not be believed. And this I have more cause to fear, for that I know how difficultly and hardly I myself would have believed another man telling the same, if I had not presently seen it with mine own eyes. For it must needs be that how far a thing is dissonant and disagreeing from the guise and trade of the hearers, so far shall it be out of their belief. Howbeit, a wise and indifferent esteemer of things will not greatly marvel perchance, seeing all their other laws and customs do so much differ from ours, if the use also of gold and silver among them be applied rather to their own fashions than to ours. I mean, in that they occupy not money themselves, but keep it for that chance; which as it may happen, so it may be that it shall never come to pass.

In the meantime gold and silver, whereof money is made, they do so use as none of them doth more esteem it than the very nature of the thing deserveth. And then

who doth not plainly see how far it is under iron? as
without the which men can no better live than without
fire and water; whereas to gold and silver nature hath
given no use that we may not well lack, if that the folly
of men had not set it in higher estimation for the rare-
ness' sake. But, of the contrary part, nature, as a most
tender and loving mother, hath placed the best and most
necessary things open abroad, as the air, the water, and
the earth itself; and hath removed and hid farthest from
us vain and unprofitable things. Therefore if these metals among them should be fast locked up in some tower,
it might be suspected that the prince and the council
(as the people is ever foolishly imagining) intended by
some subtlety to deceive the commons and to take some
profit of it to themselves. Furthermore, if they should
make thereof plate and such other finely and cunningly
wrought stuff; if at any time they should have occasion
to break it and melt it again and therewith to pay their
soldiers wages, they see and perceive very well that men
would be loath to part from those things that they once
begun to have pleasure and delight in.

To remedy all this, they have found out a means,
which, as it is agreeable to all their other laws and customs, so it is from ours, where gold is so much set by and
so diligently kept, very far discrepant and repugnant;
and therefore incredible, but only to them that be wise.
For whereas they eat and drink in earthen and glass vessels, which indeed be curiously and properly made, and
yet be of very small value; of gold and silver they make
commonly chamber-pots and other like vessels that serve
for most vile uses, not only in their common halls but in
every man's private house. Furthermore of the same
metals they make great chains with fetters and gyves,

wherein they tie their bondmen. Finally, whosoever for any offence be infamed, by their ears hang rings of gold, upon their fingers they wear rings of gold, and about their necks chains of gold, and in conclusion their heads be tied about with gold. Thus, by all means that may be, they procure to have gold and silver among them in reproach and infamy. And therefore these metals, which other nations do as grievously and sorrowfully forego, as in a manner from their own lives; if they should altogether at once be taken from the Utopians, no man there would think that he had lost the worth of one farthing.

They gather also pearls by the seaside and diamonds and carbuncles upon certain rocks, and yet they seek not for them; but by chance finding them they cut and polish them, and therewith they deck their young infants; which, like as in the first years of their childhood they make much and be fond and proud of such ornaments, so when they be a little more grown in years and discretion, perceiving that none but children do wear such toys and trifles, they lay them away even of their own shamefastness without any bidding of their parents; even as our children when they wax big, do cast away nuts, brooches, and puppets. Therefore these laws and customs, which be so far different from all other nations, how divers fancies also and minds they do cause, did I never so plainly perceive as in the ambassadors of the Anemolians.

Anemolians; from ἀνεμώλιος = windy

These ambassadors came to Amaurote whiles I was there; and because they came to entreat of great and weighty matters, those three citizens apiece out of every city were come thither before them. But all the ambassadors of the next countries which had been there before and knew the fashions and manners of the Utopians, among whom they perceived no honor given to sumptuous and costly apparel, silks to be contemned, gold also to be infamed and reproachful, were wont to come thither in very homely and simple apparel; but the Anemolians, because they dwell far thence and had very little acquaintance with them, hearing that they were all apparelled alike, and that very rudely and homely, thinking them not to have the things which they did not wear, being therefore more proud than wise, determined in the gorgeousness of their apparel to represent very gods, and with the bright shining and glistening of their gay clothing to dazzle the eyes of the silly poor Utopians. So there came in three ambassadors with a hundred servants all apparelled in changeable colors, the most of them in silks; the ambassadors themselves (for at home in their own country they were noblemen) in cloth of gold, with great chains of gold, with gold hanging at their ears, with gold rings upon their fingers, with brooches and aglets of gold upon their caps, which glistered full of pearls and precious stones; to be short, trimmed and adorned with all those things which among the Utopians were either the punishment of bondmen, or the reproach of infamed persons, or else trifles for young children to play withal. Therefore it would have done a man good at his heart to have seen how proudly they displayed their peacock feathers, how much they made of their painted sheaths, and how loftily they set forth and advanced themselves, when they compared their gallant apparel with the poor raiment of the Utopians; for all the people were swarmed forth into the streets. And on the other side it was no less pleasure to consider how much they were deceived, and how far they missed of their purpose; being contrary ways taken

aglets = pendants

than they thought they should have been; for to the eyes of all the Utopians, except very few which had been in other countries for some reasonable cause, all that gorgeousness of apparel seemed shameful and reproachful, insomuch that they most reverently saluted the vilest and most abject of them for lords; passing over the ambassadors themselves without any honor, judging them by their wearing of golden chains to be bondmen. Yea, you should have seen children also that had cast away their pearls and precious stones, when they saw the like sticking upon the ambassadors' caps, dig and push their mothers under the sides, saying thus to them: 'Look, mother, how great a lubber doth yet wear pearls and precious stones, as though he were a little child still!' But the mother, yea, and that also in good earnest: 'Peace, son,' saith she, 'I think he be some of the ambassadors' fools.' Some found fault at their golden chains as to no use nor purpose, being so small and weak that a bondman might easily break them; and again so wide and large that when it pleased him he might cast them off and run away at liberty whither he would.

But when the ambassadors had been there a day or two and saw so great abundance of gold so lightly esteemed, yea, in no less reproach than it was with them in honour; and, besides that, more gold in the chains and gyves of one fugitive bondman than all the costly ornaments of them three was worth, they began to abate their courage and for very shame laid away all that gorgeous array whereof they were so proud, and specially when they had talked familiarly with the Utopians and had learned all their fashions and opinions. For they marvel that any men be so foolish as to have delight and pleasure in the glistering of a little trifling stone which may behold any of the stars or else the sun itself; or that any man is so mad as to count himself the nobler for the smaller or finer thread of wool, which self-same wool (be it now in never so fine a spun thread) did once a sheep wear; and yet was she all that time no other thing than a sheep.

They marvel also that gold, which of the own nature is a thing so unprofitable, is now among all people in so high estimation that man himself, by whom, yea and for the use of whom, it is so much set by, is in much less estimation than the gold itself: insomuch that a lumpish, blockheaded churl, and which hath no more wit than an ass, yea, and as full of naughtiness and foolishness, shall have nevertheless many wise and good men in subjection and bondage, only for this, because he hath a great heap of gold; which if it should be taken from him by any fortune, or by some subtle wile of the law (which no less than fortune doth raise up the low and pluck down the high) and be given to the most vile slave and abject drevell of all his household, then shortly after he *drevell = drudge* shall go into the service of his servant as an augmentation or an overplus beside his money. But they much more marvel at and detest the madness of them which to those rich men, in whose debt and danger they be not, do give almost divine honors for none other consideration but because they be rich; and yet knowing them to be such niggish penny-fathers that they be sure as long *niggish penny-* as they live not the worth of one farthing of that heap of *fathers = niggardly* gold shall come to them. *misers*

These and such like opinions have they conceived, partly by education, being brought up in that commonwealth whose laws and customs be far different from these kinds of folly, and partly by good literature and learning. For though there be not many in every city which be exempt and discharged of all other labors and appointed only to learning; that is to say, such in whom even from their very childhood they have perceived a singular towardness, a fine wit, and a mind apt to good learning; yet all in their childhood be instruct in learning. And the better part of the people, both men and women, throughout all their whole life do bestow in learning those spare hours which we said they have vacant from bodily labors. They be taught learning in their own native tongue; for it is both copious in words and also pleasant to the ear, and for the utterance of a man's mind very perfect and sure. The most part of all that side of the world useth the same language, saving that among the Utopians it is finest and purest; and according to the diversity of the countries it is diversely altered.

Of all these philosophers whose names be here famous in this part of the world to us known, before our coming thither, not as much as the fame of any of them was common among them; and yet in music, logic, arithmetic, and geometry they have found out in a manner all that our ancient philosophers have taught. But as they in all things be almost equal to our old ancient clerks, so our new logicians in subtle inventions have far passed and gone beyond them. For they have not devised one of all those rules of restrictions, amplifications, and suppositions, very wittily invented in the Small Logicals, which here our children in every place do learn. Furthermore, they were never yet able to find out the second intentions; insomuch that none of them all could ever see man himself in common, as they call him; though he be (as you know) bigger than ever was any giant, yea, and pointed to of us even with our finger. But they be in the course of the stars and the movings of the heavenly spheres very expert and cunning. They have also wittily excogitated and devised instruments of divers fashions, wherein is exactly comprehended and contained the movings and situations of the sun, the moon, and of all the other stars which appear in their horizon. But as for the amities and dissensions of the planets and all that deceitful divination by the stars, they never as much as dreamed thereof. Rains, winds, and other courses of tempests they know before by certain tokens, which they have learned by long use and observation. But of the causes of all these things, and of the ebbing, flowing, and saltiness of the sea, and finally of the original beginning and nature of heaven and of the world, they hold partly the same opinions that our old philosophers hold, and partly, as our philosophers vary among themselves, so they also, whiles they bring new reasons of things, do disagree from all them, and yet among themselves in all points they do not accord.

In that part of philosophy which entreateth of manners and virtue, their reasons and opinions agree with ours. They dispute of the good qualities of the soul, of the body, and of fortune, and whether the name of goodness may be applied to all these or only to the endowments and gifts of the soul. They reason of virtue and pleasure. But the chief and principal question is in what thing, be it one or more, the felicity of man consisteth. But in this point they seem almost too much given and inclined to the opinion of them which defend pleasure; wherein they determine either all or the chiefest part of man's felicity to rest. And (which is more to be marvelled at) the defence of this so dainty and delicate an opinion they fetch even from their grave, sharp, bitter, and rigorous religion. For they never dispute of felicity or blessedness but they join to the reasons of philosophy certain principles taken out of religion; without the which, to the investigation of true felicity, they think reason of itself weak and unperfect. Those principles be these and such like: that the soul is immortal, and by the bountiful goodness of God ordained to felicity; that to our virtues and good deeds rewards be appointed after this life, and to our evil deeds punishments. Though these be pertaining to religion, yet they think it meet that they should be believed and granted by proofs of reason. But if these principles were condemned and disannulled, then without any delay they pronounce no man to be so foolish, which would not do all his diligence and endeavor to obtain pleasure by right or wrong, only avoiding this inconvenience, that the less pleasure should not be a let or hindrance to the bigger; or that he labored not for that pleasure which would bring after it displeasure, grief, and sorrow. For they judge it extreme madness to follow sharp and painful virtue, and not only to banish the pleasure of life, but also willingly to suffer grief without any hope of profit thereof. For what profit can there be, if a man, when he hath passed over all his life unpleasantly, that is to say, wretchedly, shall have no reward after his death?

But now, sir, they think not felicity to rest in all pleasure, but only in that pleasure that is good and honest; and that hereto, as to perfect blessedness, our nature is allured and drawn even of virtue; whereto only they that be of the contrary opinion do attribute felicity. For they define virtue to be a life ordered according to nature; and that we be hereunto ordained of God; and that he doth follow the course of nature, which in desiring and refusing things is ruled by reason. Furthermore, that reason doth chiefly and principally kindle in men the love and veneration of the Divine Majesty, of whose goodness it is that we be, and that we be in possibility to attain felicity. And that, secondarily, it moveth and provoketh us to lead our life out of care in joy and mirth, and to help all other, in respect of the society of nature, to obtain the same. For there was never man so earnest and painful a follower of virtue and hater of pleasure, that would so enjoin you labours, watchings, and fastings, but he would also exhort you to ease and lighten to your power the lack and misery of others; praising the same as a deed of humanity and pity. Then if it be a point of humanity for man to bring health and comfort to man, and specially (which is a virtue most peculiarly belonging to man) to mitigate and assuage the grief of others, and by taking from them the sorrow and heaviness of life to restore them to joy, that is to say, to pleasure; why may it not then be said that nature doth provoke every man to do the same to himself?

For a joyful life, that is to say, a pleasant life, is either evil; and if it be so, then thou shouldst not only help no man thereto, but rather as much as in thee lieth help all men from it, as noisome and hurtful; or else, if thou not only mayst but also of duty art bound to procure it to others, why not chiefly to thyself, to whom thou art bound to show as much favor as to other? For when nature biddeth thee to be good and gentle to other, she commandeth thee not to be cruel and ungentle to thyself. Therefore even very nature (say they) prescribeth to us a joyful life, that is to say, pleasure as the end of all our operations. And they define virtue to be life ordered according to the prescript of nature. But in that that nature doth allure and provoke men one to help another to live merrily (which surely she doth not without a good cause; for no man is so far above the lot of man's state or condition that nature doth cark and care for him only, which equally favoreth all that be comprehended under the communion of one shape, form, and fashion), verily she commandeth thee to use diligent circumspection, that thou do not so seek for thine own commodities, that thou procure others incommodities.

Wherefore their opinion is, that not only covenants and bargains made among private men ought to be well and faithfully fulfilled, observed, and kept, but also common laws; which either a good prince hath justly published, or else the people, neither oppressed with tyranny, neither deceived by fraud and guile, hath by their common consent constitute and ratified, concerning the partition of the commodities of life,— that is to say, the matter of pleasure. These laws not offended, it is wisdom that thou look to thine own wealth. And to do the same for the commonwealth is no less than thy duty, if thou bearest any reverent love or any natural zeal and affection to thy native country. But to go *let = hinder* about to let another man of his pleasure whiles thou procurest thine own, that is open wrong. Contrariwise, to withdraw something from thyself to give to other, that is a point of humanity and gentleness, which never taketh away so much commodity as it bringeth again. For it is recompensed with the return of benefits; and the conscience of the good deed, with the remembrance of the thankful love and benevolence of them to whom thou hast done it, doth bring more pleasure to thy mind than that which thou hast withholden from thyself could have brought to thy body. Finally (which to a godly disposed and a religious mind is easy to be persuaded), God recompenseth the gift of a short and small pleasure with great and everlasting joy. Therefore, the matter diligently weighed and considered, thus they think: that all our actions, and in them the virtues themselves, be referred at the last to pleasure as their end and felicity.

Pleasure they call every motion and state of the body or mind wherein man hath naturally delectation. Appetite they join to nature, and that not without a good cause. For like as not only the senses, but also right reason, coveteth whatsoever is naturally pleasant; so that it may be gotten without wrong or injury, not letting or debarring a greater pleasure, nor causing painful labor; even so those things that men by vain imagination do feign against nature to be pleasant (as though it lay in their power to change the things as they do the names of things), all such pleasures they believe to be of so small help and furtherance to felicity that they count them great let and hindrance; because that, in whom they have once taken place, all his mind they possess with a false opinion of pleasure; so that there is no place left for true and natural delectations. For there be many things which of their own nature contain no pleasantness, yea the most part of them much grief and sorrow; and yet, through the perverse and malicious flickering enticements of lewd and unhonest desires, be taken not only for special and sovereign pleasures, but also be counted among the chief causes of life.

In this counterfeit kind of pleasure they put them that I speak of before; which, the better gown they have on, the better men they think themselves: in the which thing they do twice err, for they be no less deceived in that they think their gown the better, than they be in that they think themselves the better. For if you consider the profitable use of the garment, why should wool of a finer spun thread be thought better than the wool of a coarse spun thread? Yet they, as though the one did pass the *avaunce = pride* other by nature and not by their mistaking, avaunce themselves and think the price of their own persons thereby greatly increased. And therefore the honor, which in a coarse gown they durst not have looked for, they require as it were of duty, for their finer gown's sake. And if they be passed by without reverence, they take it angrily and disdainfully.

And again, is it not a like madness to take a pride in vain and unprofitable honors? For what natural or true pleasure dost thou take of another man's bare head or bowed knees? Will this ease the pain of thy knees, or remedy the frenzy of thy head? In this image of counterfeit pleasure, they be of a marvelous madness, which for the opinion of nobility rejoice much in their own conceit, because it was their fortune to come of such ancestors whose stock of long time hath been counted rich (for now nobility is nothing else), specially rich in lands. And though their ancestors left them not one foot of land, or else they themselves have pissed it against the walls, yet they think themselves not the less noble therefore of one hair.

In this number also they count them that take pleasure and delight (as I said) in gems and precious stones, and think themselves almost gods if they chance to get an excellent one, specially of that kind which in that time of their own countrymen is had in highest estimation; for one kind of stone keepeth not his price still in all countries and at all times. Nor they buy them not but taken out of the gold and bare; no, nor so neither, before they have made the seller to swear that he will warrant and assure it to be a true stone and no counterfeit gem. Such care they take lest a counterfeit stone should deceive their eyes in the stead of a right stone. But why shouldst thou not take even as much pleasure in beholding a counterfeit stone which thine eye cannot discern from a right stone? They should both be of like value to thee, even as to a blind man. What shall I say of them that keep superfluous riches, to take delectation only in the beholding and not in the use or occupying thereof? Do they take true pleasure, or else be they deceived with false pleasure? Or of them that be in a contrary vice, hiding the gold which they shall never occupy nor peradventure never see more; and, whiles they take care lest they shall lose it, do lose it indeed? For what is it else, when they hide it in the ground, taking it both from their own use and perchance from all other men's also? And yet thou, when thou hast hid thy treasure, as one out of all care hoppest for joy; the which treasure, if it should chance to be stolen and thou, ignorant of the theft, shouldst die ten years after; all that ten years' space that thou livedest after thy money was stolen, what matter was it to thee whether it had been taken away, or else safe as thou leftest it? Truly both ways like profit came to thee.

To these so foolish pleasures they join dicers, whose madness they know by hearsay and not by use; hunters also, and hawkers. For what pleasure is there (say they) in casting the dice upon a table, which thou hast done so often that if there were any pleasure in it, yet the oft use might make thee weary thereof? Or what delight can there be, and not rather displeasure, in hearing the barking and howling of dogs? Or what greater pleasure is there to be felt when a dog followeth an hare than when a dog followeth a dog? for one thing is done in both; that is to say, running; if thou hast pleasure therein. But if the hope of slaughter and the expectation of tearing in pieces the beast doth please thee, thou shouldst rather be moved with pity to see a silly innocent hare murdered of a dog, the weak of the stronger, the fearful of the fierce, the innocent of the cruel and unmerciful. Therefore all this exercise of hunting, as a thing unworthy to be used of free men, the Utopians have rejected to their butchers; to the which craft (as we said before) they appoint their bondmen. For they count hunting the lowest, vilest, and most abject part of butchery; and the other parts of it more profitable and more honest, as which do bring much more commodity; and do kill beasts only for necessity, whereas the hunter seeketh nothing but pleasure of the silly and woeful beast's slaughter and murder; the which pleasure in beholding death they think doth rise in the very beasts either of a cruel affection of mind or else to be changed in continuance of time into cruelty by long use of so cruel a pleasure. This therefore and all such like, which be innumerable, though the common sort of people doth take them for pleasures, yet they, seeing there is no natural pleasantness in them, do plainly determine them to have no affinity with true and right pleasure. For as touching that they do commonly move the sense with delectation (which seemeth to be a work of pleasure) this doth nothing diminish their opinion. For not the nature of the thing but their perverse and lewd custom is the cause hereof; which causeth them to accept bitter or sour things for sweet things, even as women with child, in their vitiate and corrupt taste, think pitch and tallow sweeter than any honey. Howbeit no man's judgment, depraved and corrupt either by sickness or by custom, can change the nature of pleasure more than it can do the nature of other things.

They make divers kinds of true pleasures; for some they attribute to the soul and some to the body. To the soul they give intelligence and that delectation that cometh of the contemplation of truth. Hereunto is joined the pleasant remembrance of the good life past.

The pleasure of the body they divide into two parts. The first is when delectation is sensibly felt and perceived, which many times chanceth by the renewing and refreshing of those parts which our natural heat drieth up: this cometh by meat and drink, and sometimes whiles those things be voided whereof is in the body over-great abundance. This pleasure is felt when we do our natural easement or when we be doing the act of generation, or when the itching of any part is eased with rubbing or scratching. Sometimes pleasure riseth, exhibiting to any member nothing that it desireth, nor taking from it any pain that it feeleth; which for all that tickleth and moveth our senses with a certain secret efficacy, but with a manifest motion, and turneth them to it; as is that which cometh of music.

The second part of bodily pleasure they say is that which consisteth and resteth in the quiet and upright state of the body. And that truly is every man's own proper health, intermingled and disturbed with no grief.

For this, if it be not letted nor assaulted with no grief, is delectable of itself, though it be moved with no external or outward pleasure. For though it be not so plain and manifest to the sense as the greedy lust of eating and drinking, yet nevertheless many take it for the chiefest pleasure. All the Utopians grant it to be a right great pleasure, and, as you would say, the foundation and ground of all pleasures, as which even alone is able to make the state and condition of life delectable and pleasant; and, it being once taken away, there is no place left for any pleasure. For to be without grief, not having health, that they call unsensibility and not pleasure. The Utopians have long ago rejected and condemned the opinion of them which said that steadfast and quiet health (for this question also hath been diligently debated among them) ought not therefore to be counted a pleasure, because they say it cannot be presently and sensibly perceived and felt by some outward motion. But, of the contrary part, now they agree almost all in this, that health is a most sovereign pleasure. For seeing that in sickness (say they) is grief, which is a mortal enemy to pleasure, even as sickness is to health, why should not then pleasure be in the quietness of health? For they say it maketh nothing to this matter whether you say that sickness is a grief, or that in sickness is grief, for all cometh to one purpose. For whether health be a pleasure itself or a necessary cause of pleasure, as fire is of heat, truly both ways it followeth that they cannot be without pleasure that be in perfect health. Furthermore, whiles we eat (say they) then health, which began to be appaired, fighteth by the help of food against hunger; in the which fight whiles health by little and little getteth the upper hand, that same proceeding, and (as you

would say) that onwardness to the wont strength ministreth that pleasure whereby we be so refreshed. Health
therefore, which in the conflict is joyful, shall it not be
merry when it hath gotten the victory? But as soon as it
hath recovered the pristinate strength, which thing only
in all the fight it coveted, shall it incontinent be astonied?
Nor shall it not know nor embrace the own wealth and
goodness? For that it is said health cannot be felt, this,
they think, is nothing true. For what man waking, say
they, feeleth not himself in health but he that is not? Is
there any man so possessed with stonish insensibility, or
with the sleeping sickness, that he will not grant health
to be acceptable to him and delectable? But what other
thing is delectation than that which by another name is
called pleasure?

They embrace chiefly the pleasures of the mind, for
them they count the chiefest and most principal of all.
The chief part of them they think doth come of the exercise of virtue and conscience of good life. Of these
pleasures that the body ministreth they give the pre-
eminence to health. For the delight of eating and drinking and whatsoever hath any like pleasantness, they determine to be pleasures much to be desired, but no other
ways than for health's sake. For such things of their own
proper nature be not pleasant but in that they resist sickness privily stealing on. Therefore, like as it is a wise
man's part rather to avoid sickness than to wish for medicines, and rather to drive away and put to flight careful
griefs than to call for comfort, so it is much better not
to need this kind of pleasure than in sealing the contrary
grief to be eased of the same. The which kind of pleasure
if any man take for his felicity, that man must needs
grant that then he shall be in most felicity if he live that

life which is led in continual hunger, thirst, itching, eating, drinking, scratching, and rubbing; the which life how not only foul it is but also miserable and wretched, who perceiveth not? These doubtless be the basest pleasures of all, as unpure and unperfect; for they never come but accompanied with their contrary griefs, as with the pleasure of eating is joined hunger, and that after no very equal sort. For of these two the grief is both the more vehement and also of longer continuance. For it riseth before the pleasure and endeth not until the pleasure die with it.

Wherefore such pleasures they think not greatly to be set by, but in that they be necessary. Howbeit they have delight also in these, and thankfully knowledge the tender love of mother nature, which with most pleasant delectation allureth her children to that which of necessity they be driven often [to] use. For how wretched and miserable should our life be if these daily griefs of hunger and thirst could not be driven away but with bitter potions and sour medicines, as the other diseases be wherewith we be seldomer troubled? But beauty, strength, nimbleness, these, as peculiar and pleasant gifts of nature, they make much of. But those pleasures which be received by the ears, the eyes, and the nose, which nature willeth to be proper and peculiar to man (for no other kind of living beasts doth behold the fairness and the beauty of the world, or is moved with any respect of savours, but only for the diversity of meats, neither perceiveth the concordant and discordant distances of sounds and tunes) these pleasures (I say) they accept and allow as certain pleasant rejoicings of life. But in all *cautel = precaution* things this cautel they use, that a less pleasure hinder not a bigger, and that the pleasure be no cause of displeasure;

which they think to follow of necessity, if the pleasure
be unhonest. But yet to despise the comeliness of beauty,
to waste the bodily strength, to turn nimbleness into
sluggishness, to consume and make feeble the body with
fasting, to do injury to health, and to reject the other
pleasant motions of nature (unless a man neglect these
his commodities whiles he doth with a fervent zeal procure the wealth of others, or the common profit, for the
which pleasure forborne he is in hope of a greater pleasure of God) : else for a vain shadow of virtue, for the
wealth and profit of no man to punish himself, or to the
intent he may be able courageously to suffer adversities
which perchance shall never come to him: this to do
they think it a point of extreme madness and a token of
a man cruelly-minded towards himself and unkind toward nature, as one so disdaining to be in her danger that
he renounceth and refuseth all her benefits.

This is their sentence and opinion of virtue and pleasure. And they believe that by man's reason none can be
found truer than this, unless any godlier be inspired into
man from heaven. Wherein whether they believe well
or no, neither the time doth suffer us to discuss, neither
it is now necessary; for we have taken upon us to show
and declare their lores and ordinances, and not to defend   *lores = doctrines*
them.

But this thing I believe verily: howsoever these decrees be, that there is in no place of the world neither a
more excellent people, neither a more flourishing commonwealth. They be light and quick of body, full of
activity and nimbleness, and of more strength than a
man would judge them by their stature, which for all
that is not too low. And though their soil be not very
fruitful nor their air very wholesome, yet against the

air they so defend them with temperate diet, and so order and husband their ground with diligent travail, that in no country is greater increase and plenty of corn and cattle, nor men's bodies of longer life and subject or apt to fewer diseases. There, therefore, a man may see well and diligently exploited and furnished not only those things which husbandmen do commonly in other countries, as by craft and cunning to remedy the barrenness of the ground, but also a whole wood by the hands of the people plucked up by the roots in one place and set again in another place; wherein was had regard and consideration not of plenty but of commodious carriage, that wood and timber might be nigher to the sea or the rivers or the cities. For it is less labor and business to carry grain far by land than wood. The people be gentle, merry, quick, and fine-witted, delighting in quietness, and when need requireth, able to abide and suffer much bodily labor; else they be not greatly desirous and fond of it, but in the exercise and study of the mind they be never weary.

When they had heard me speak of the Greek literature or learning (for in Latin there was nothing that I thought they would greatly allow besides historians and poets), they made wonderful earnest and importunate suit unto me that I would teach and instruct them in that tongue and learning. I began therefore to read unto them, at the first, truly, more because I would not seem to refuse the labor than that I hoped that they would anything profit therein. But when I had gone forward a little and perceived incontinent by their diligence that my labor should not be bestowed in vain; for they began so easily to fashion their letters, so plainly to pronounce the words, so quickly to learn by heart, and so surely to rehearse the same, that I marveled at it; saving that the most part of them were fine and chosen wits and of ripe age, picked out of the company of the learned men, which not only of their own free and voluntary will but also by the commandment of the council undertook to learn this language. Therefore in less than three years' space there was nothing in the Greek tongue that they lacked. They were able to read good authors without any stay, if the book were not false.

This kind of learning, as I suppose, they took so much the sooner because it is somewhat alliant to them. For I think that this nation took their beginning of the Greeks, because their speech, which in all other points is not much unlike the Persian tongue, keepeth divers signs and tokens of the Greek language in the names of their cities and of their magistrates. They have of me (for, when I was determined to enter into my fourth voyage, I cast into the ship in the stead of merchandise, a pretty fardel *fardel = bundle* of books, because I intended to come again rather never than shortly) the most part of Plato's works, more of Aristotle's, also Theophrastus' *Of Plants*, but in divers places (which I am sorry for) unperfect. For whiles we were sailing, a marmoset chanced upon the book as it was negligently laid by, which, wantonly playing therewith, plucked out certain leaves and tore them in pieces. Of them that have written the grammar, they have only Lascaris; for Theodorus I carried not with me, nor never a dictionary but Hesychius and Dioscorides. They set great store by Plutarch's books; and they be delighted with Lucian's merry conceits and jests. Of the poets they have Aristophanes, Homer, Euripides, and Sophocles in Aldus' small print. Of the historians they have Thucydides, Herodotus, and Herodian. Also my companion, Tricius Apinatus, carried with him physic books: certain small works of Hippocrates and Galen's *Micro-techne*, the which book they have in great estimation. For though there be almost no nation under heaven that hath less need of physic than they, yet, this notwithstanding, physic is nowhere in greater honor, because they count the knowledge of it among the goodliest and most profitable parts of philosophy. For whiles they by the help of this philosophy search out the secret mysteries of nature, they think that they not only receive thereby wonderful great pleasure but also obtain great thanks and favor of the Author and Maker thereof; whom they think, according to the fashion of other artificers, to have set forth the marvelous and gorgeous frame of the world for man to behold, whom only he hath made of wit and capacity to consider and understand the excellency of so great a work. And therefore, say they, doth he bear more good will and love to the curious and diligent beholder and viewer of his work and marveler at the same than he doth to him which like a very beast without wit and reason, or as one without sense or moving, hath no regard to so great and so wonderful a spectacle.

The wits, therefore, of the Utopians, inured and exercised in learning, be marvelous quick in the invention of feats helping anything to the advantage and wealth of life. Howbeit, two feats they may thank us for; that is, the science of imprinting and the craft of making paper: and yet not only us but chiefly and principally themselves. For when we showed to them Aldus his print in books of paper and told them of the stuff whereof paper is made and of the feat of graving letters, speaking somewhat more than we could plainly declare (for there was none of us that knew perfectly either the one or the other), they forthwith very wittily conjectured the thing. And whereas before they wrote only in skins, in barks of trees, and in reeds, now they have attempted to make paper and to imprint letters. And though at the first it proved not all of the best, yet by often assaying the same they shortly got the feat of both, and have so brought the matter about that if they had copies of Greek authors they could lack no books. But now they have no more than I rehearsed before; saving that by printing of books they have multiplied and increased the same into many thousand of copies.

Whosoever cometh thither to see the land, being excellent in any gift of wit, or through much and long journeying well-experienced and seen in the knowledge of many countries (for the which cause we were very welcome to them), him they receive and entertain won- *wonders =* ders gently and lovingly; for they have delight to hear *wondrously* what is done in every land. Howbeit, very few merchantmen come thither. For what should they bring thither? unless it were iron; or else gold and silver, which they had rather carry home again. Also such things as are to be carried out of their land, they think it more wisdom to carry that gear forth themselves than that others should come thither to fetch it, to the intent they may the better know the out-lands of every side them *ure the feat =* and keep in ure the feat and knowledge of sailing. *use the art*

Of Bondmen, sick Persons, Wedlock and divers other matters.

THEY neither make bondmen of prisoners taken in battle, unless it be in battle that they fought themselves, nor bondmen's children, nor, to be short, any man whom they can get out of another country, though he were there a bondman; but either such as among themselves for heinous offences be punished with bondage, or else such as in the cities of other lands for great trespasses be condemned to death. And of this sort of bondmen they have most store, for many of them they bring home, sometimes paying very little for them; yea, most commonly getting them for gramercy. These sorts of bondmen they keep not only in continual work and labor but also in bonds. But their own men they handle hardest, whom they judge more desperate and to have deserved greater punishment, because they, being so godly brought up to virtue in so excellent a commonwealth could not for all that be refrained from misdoing.

Another kind of bondmen they have, when a vile drudge, being a poor laborer in another country doth choose of his own free will to be a bondman among them. These they handle and order honestly, and entertain almost as gently as their own free citizens; saving that they put them to a little more labor, as thereto accustomed. If any such be disposed to depart thence (which seldom is seen) they neither hold him against his will, neither send him away with empty hands.

The sick (as I said) they see to with great affection, and let nothing at all pass concerning either physic or good diet, whereby they may be restored again to their health. Them that be sick of incurable diseases they comfort with sitting by them, with talking with them, and, to be short, with all manner of helps that may be. But if the diseases be not only incurable but also full of continual pain and anguish, then the priests and the magistrates exhort the man, seeing he is not able to do any duty of life, and by overliving his own death is noisome and irksome to other and grievous to himself, that he will determine with himself no longer to cherish that pestilent and painful disease; and, seeing his life is to him but a torment, that he will not be unwilling to die, but rather take a good hope to him and either dispatch himself out of that painful life, as out of a prison or a rack of torment, or else suffer himself willingly to be rid out of it by other. And in so doing they tell him he shall do wisely, seeing by his death he shall lose no commodity but end his pain. And because in that act he shall follow the counsel of the priests, that is to say, of the interpreters of God's will and pleasure, they show him that he shall do like a godly and a virtuous man. They that be thus persuaded finish their lives willingly, either with hunger, or else die in their sleep without any feeling of death. But they cause none such to die against his will; nor they use no less diligence and attendance about him; believing this to be an honorable death. Else he that killeth himself before that the priests and the council have allowed the cause of his death, him, as unworthy both of the earth and of fire, they cast unburied into some stinking marsh.

The woman is not married before she be eighteen years old. The man is four years elder before he marry. If either the man or the woman be proved to have bodily offended, before their marriage, with another, he or she, whether it be, is sharply punished; and both the offenders be forbidden ever after in all their life to marry unless the fault be forgiven by the prince's pardon. But both the good man and the good wife of the house where that offence was done, as being slack and negligent in looking to their charge, be in danger of great reproach and infamy. That offence is so sharply punished because they perceive that unless they be diligently kept from the liberty of this vice, few will join together in the love of marriage; wherein all the life must be led with one, and also all the griefs and displeasures that come therewith must patiently be taken and borne.

Furthermore, in choosing wives and husbands they observe earnestly and straitly a custom which seemed to us very fond and foolish. For a sad and an honest matron showeth the woman, be she maid or widow, naked to the wooer; and likewise a sage and discreet man exhibiteth the wooer naked to the woman. At this custom we laughed and disallowed it as foolish. But they on the other part do greatly wonder at the folly of all other nations, which in buying a colt, where as a little money is in hazard, be so chary and circumspect that though he be almost all bare, yet they will not buy him unless the saddle and all the harness be taken off, lest under those coverings be hid some gall or sore; and yet in choosing a wife, which shall be either pleasure or displeasure to them all their life after, they be so reckless that, all the residue of the woman's body being covered with clothes, they esteem her scarcely by one handbreadth (for they can see no more but her face); and so do join her to them not without great jeopardy of evil agreeing together, if anything in her body afterward do offend and mislike them. For all men be not so wise as to have respect to the virtuous conditions of the party; and the endowments of the body cause the virtues of the mind more to be esteemed and regarded, yea, even in the marriages of wise men. Verily so foul deformity may be hid under those coverings that it may quite alienate and take away the man's mind from his wife, when it shall not be lawful for their bodies to be separate again. If such deformity happen by any chance after the marriage is consummate and finished; well, there is no remedy but patience. Every man must take his fortune, well a worth! But it were well done that a law were made whereby all such deceits might be eschewed and avoided beforehand. And this were they constrained more earnestly to look upon, because they only of the nations in that part of the world be content every man with one wife apiece, and matrimony is there never broken but by death, except adultery break the bond or else the intolerable wayward manners of either party. For if either of them find themself for any such cause grieved, they may by the license of the council change and take another. But the other party liveth ever after in infamy and out of wedlock. But for the husband to put away his wife for no fault but for that some mishap is fallen to her body, this by no means they will suffer. For they judge it a great point of cruelty that anybody in their most need of help and comfort should be cast off and forsaken; and that old age, which both bringeth sickness with it and is a sickness itself, should unkindly and unfaithfully be dealt withal. But now and then it chanceth, whereas the man and the woman cannot well agree between themselves, both of them finding other with whom they hope to live more quietly and merrily, that they by the full consent of them both be divorced asunder and new married to other; but that not without the authority of the council, which agreeth to no divorces before they and their wives have diligently tried and examined the matter. Yea and then also they be loath to consent to it, because they know this to be the next way to break love between man and wife, to be in easy hope of a new marriage.

Utopia

Breakers of wedlock be punished with most grievous bondage. And if both the offenders were married, then the parties which in that behalf have suffered wrong be divorced from the avowters if they will, and be married together, or else to whom they lust. But if either of them both do still continue in love toward so unkind a bedfellow, the use of wedlock is not to them forbidden, if the party be disposed to follow in toiling and drudgery the person which for that offence is condemned to bondage. And very oft it chanceth that the repentance of the one and the earnest diligence of the other doth so move the prince with pity and compassion that he restoreth the bond-person from servitude to liberty and freedom again. But if the same party be taken eftsoons in that fault, there is no other way but death.

To other trespasses there is no prescript punishment appointed by any law, but according to the heinousness of the offence or contrary, so the punishment is moderated by the discretion of the council. The husbands chastise their wives and the parents their children, unless they have done any so horrible an offence that the open punishment thereof maketh much for the advancement of honest manners. But most commonly the most heinous faults be punished with the incommodity of bondage; for that they suppose to be to the offenders no less grief and to the commonwealth more profitable than if they should hastily put them to death and make them out of the way. For there cometh more profit of their labor than of their death, and by their example they fear other the longer from like offences. But if they, being thus used, do rebel and kick again, then forsooth they be slain as desperate and wild beasts, whom neither prison nor chain could restrain and keep under. But they which

avowters =
adulterers

fear other =
frighten others

take their bondage patiently be not left all hopeless; for
after they have been broken and tamed with long miseries, if then they show such repentance whereby it may
be perceived that they be sorrier for their offence than
for their punishment, sometimes by the prince's prerogative and sometimes by the voice and consent of the
people their bondage either is mitigated or else clean
remitted and forgiven. He that moveth to advowtry is *advowtry =*
in no less danger and jeopardy than if he had committed *adultery*
advowtry indeed, for in all offences they count the intent and pretensed purpose as evil as the act or deed itself. For they think that no let ought to excuse him that
did his best to have no let.

They set great store by fools, and as it is great reproach to do to any of them hurt or injury, so they pro-
hibit not to take pleasure of foolishness, for that, they
think, doth much good to the fools. And if any man be
so sad and stern that he cannot laugh neither at their
words nor at their deeds, none of them be committed
to his tuition, for fear lest he would not order them gently and favorably enough to whom they should bring
no delectation (for other goodness in them is none),
much less any profit should they yield him.

To mock a man for his deformity, or for that he lacketh any part or limb of his body, is counted great dishonesty and reproach, not to him that is mocked but to him
that mocketh; which unwisely doth imbraid any man of *imbraid = upbraid*
that as a vice which was not in his power to eschew.
Also as they count and reckon very little wit to be in
him that regardeth not natural beauty and comeliness, so
to help the same with paintings is taken for a vain and a
wanton pride, not without great infamy. For they know
even by very experience that no comeliness of beauty

doth so highly commend and advance the wives in the conceit of their husbands as honest conditions and lowliness; for as love is oftentimes won with beauty, so it is not kept, preserved, and continued but by virtue and obedience.

They do not only fear their people from doing evil by punishments, but also allure them to virtue with rewards of honor. Therefore they set up in the market place the images of notable men and of such as have been great and bountiful benefactors to the commonwealth, for the perpetual memory of their good acts, and also that the glory and renown of the ancestors may stir and provoke their posterity to virtue. He that inordinately and ambitiously desireth promotions is left all hopeless for ever attaining any promotion as long as he liveth. They live together lovingly; for no magistrate is either haughty or fearful; fathers they be called, and like fathers they use themselves. The citizens (as it is their duty) do willingly exhibit unto them due honor, without any compulsion. Nor the prince himself is not known from the other by his apparel, nor by a crown or diadem or cap of maintenance, but by a little sheaf of corn carried before him. And so a taper of wax is borne before the bishop, whereby only he is known.

They have but few laws, for to people so instruct and _institute_ = _trained_   institute very few do suffice. Yea, this thing they chiefly reprove among other nations, that innumerable books of laws and expositions upon the same be not sufficient. But they think it against all right and justice that men should be bound to those laws which either be in number more than be able to be read or else blinder and darker than that any man can well understand them. Furthermore they utterly exclude and banish all proctors and ser-

geants at the law, which craftily handle matters and
subtly dispute of the laws, for they think it most meet
that every man should plead his own matter and tell the
same tale before the judge that he would tell to his man
of law. So shall there be less circumstance of words and
the truth shall sooner come to light; whiles the judge
with a discreet judgment doth weigh the words of him
whom no lawyer hath instruct with deceit, and whiles
he helpeth and beareth out simple wits against the false
and malicious circumversions of crafty children. This is
hard to be observed in other countries in so infinite a
number of blind and intricate laws; but in Utopia every
man is a cunning lawyer; for, as I said, they have very
few laws and the plainer and grosser that any interpretation is, that they allow as most just. For all laws (say
they) be made and published only to the intent that by
them every man should be put in remembrance of his
duty. But the crafty and subtle interpretation of them
can put very few in that remembrance (for they be but
few that do perceive them); whereas the simple, the
plain, and gross meaning of the laws is open to every
man. Else as touching the vulgar sort of the people,
which be both most in number and have most need to
know their duties, were it not as good for them that no
law were made at all as, when it is made, to bring so blind
an interpretation upon it that without great wit and long
arguing no man can discuss it? to the finding out whereof neither the gross judgment of the people can attain,
neither the whole life of them that be occupied in working for their livings can suffice thereto.

These virtues of the Utopians have caused their next
neighbors and borderers, which live free and under no
subjection (for the Utopians long ago have delivered

many of them from tyranny), to take magistrates of them, some for a year and some for five years' space; which, when the time of their office is expired they bring home again with honor and praise, and take new ones again with them into their country. These nations have undoubtedly very well and wholesomely provided for their commonwealths; for, seeing that both the making and the marring of the weal public doth depend and hang of the manners of the rulers and magistrates, what officers could they more wisely have chosen than those which cannot be led from honesty by bribes (for to them that shortly after shall depart thence into their own country money should be unprofitable), nor yet be moved either with favor or malice towards any man, as being strangers and unacquainted with the people? the which two vices of affection and avarice where they take place in judgments, incontinent they break justice, the strongest and surest bond of a commonwealth. These peoples which fetch their officers and rulers from them, the Utopians call their fellows; and other, to whom they have been beneficial, they call their friends.

As touching leagues, which in other places between country and country be so oft concluded, broken, and made again, they never make none with any nation. For to what purpose serve leagues? say they; as though nature had not set sufficient love between man and man. And whoso regardeth not nature, think you that he will pass for words? They be brought into this opinion chiefly because that in those parts of the world leagues between princes be wont to be kept and observed very slenderly. For here in Europa, and especially in these parts where the faith and religion of Christ reigneth, the majesty of leagues is everywhere esteemed holy and inviolable; partly through the justice and goodness of princes and partly through the reverence of great bishops; which, like as they make no promise themselves but they do very religiously perform the same, so they exhort all princes in any wise to abide by their promises; and them that refuse or deny so to do, by their pontifical power and authority they compel thereto. And surely they think well that it might seem a very reproachful thing, if in the leagues of them, which by a peculiar name be called faithful, faith should have no place.

But in that new-found part of the world, which is scarcely so far from us beyond the line equinoctial as our life and manners be dissident from theirs, no trust nor confidence is in leagues. But the more and holier ceremonies the league is knit up with, the sooner it is broken by some cavillation found in the words; which many times of purpose be so craftily put in and placed that the bands can never be so sure nor so strong but they will find some hole open to creep out at and to break both league and truth; the which crafty dealing, yea, the which fraud and deceit, if they should know it to be practised among private men in their bargains and contracts they would incontinent cry out at it with a sour countenance as an offence most detestable and worthy to be punished with a shameful death; yea, even very they that advance themselves authors of like counsel given to princes. Wherefore it may well be thought either that all justice is but a base and a low virtue, and which availeth itself far under the high dignity of kings; or at the leastwise that there be two justices, the one meet for the inferior sort of the people, going afoot and creeping by low on the ground, and bound down on every side with many bands, because it shall not run at rovers: the other

avaleth = lowers

a princely virtue, which like as it is of much higher majesty than the other poor justice, so also it is of much more liberty, as to the which nothing is unlawful that it lusteth after.

These manners of princes (as I said) which be there so evil keepers of leagues cause the Utopians, as I suppose, to make no leagues at all; which perchance would change their mind if they lived here. Howbeit they think that though leagues be never so faithfully observed and kept, yet the custom of making leagues was very evil begun. For this causeth men (as though nations which be separate asunder by the space of a little hill or a river were coupled together by no society or bond of nature) to think themselves born adversaries and enemies one to another; and that it is lawful for the one to seek the death and destruction of the other, if leagues were not; yea, and that, after the leagues be accorded, friendship doth not grow and increase; but the license of robbing and stealing doth still remain, as far forth as, for lack of foresight and advisement in writing the words of the league, any sentence or clause to the contrary is not therein sufficiently comprehended. But they be of a contrary opinion: that is, that no man ought to be counted an enemy which hath done no injury; and that the fellowship of nature is a strong league; and that men be better and more surely knit together by love and benevolence than by covenants of leagues, by hearty affection of mind than by words.

Of Warfare.

WAR or battle, as a thing very beastly, and yet to no kind of beasts in so much use as it is to man, they do detest and abhor; and, contrary to the custom almost of all other nations, they count nothing so much against glory as glory gotten in war. And therefore, though they do daily practise and exercise themselves in the discipline of war, and that not only the men, but also the women, upon certain appointed days, lest they should be to seek in the feat of arms if need should require; yet they never go to battle but either in the defence of their own country or to drive out of their friends' land the enemies that be come in, or by their power to deliver from the yoke and bondage of tyranny some people that be oppressed with tyranny; which thing they do of mere pity and compassion. Howbeit they send help to their friends; not ever in their defence but sometimes also to requite and revenge injuries before to them done. But this they do not unless their counsel and advice in the matter be asked whiles it is yet new and fresh. For if they find the cause probable and if the contrary part will not restore again such things as be of them justly demanded, then they be the chief authors and makers of the war; which they do not only as oft as by inroads and invasions of soldiers preys and booties be driven away, but then also much more mortally when their friends' merchants in any land, either under the pretence of unjust laws or else by the wresting and wrong understanding of good laws, do sustain an unjust accusation under the color of justice. Neither the battle which the Utopians fought for the Nephelogetes against the Alaopolitanes a little before our time was made for any other cause but that the Nephelogete merchantmen, as the Utopians thought, suffered wrong of the Alaopolitanes under the pretence of right. But whether it were right or wrong, it was with so cruel and mortal war revenged, the countries round about joining their help and power

Nephelogetes; from νεψέλη, cloudy, and γῆ, land

Alaopolitanes; from ἀλαός, blind, and πόλις, city

to the puissance and malice of both parties, that most flourishing and wealthy peoples being some of them shrewdly shaken and some of them sharply beaten, the mischiefs were not finished nor ended until the Alaopolitanes at the last were yielded up as bondmen into the jurisdiction of the Nephelogetes, for the Utopians fought not this war for themselves. And yet the Nephelogetes before the war, when the Alaopolitanes flourished in wealth were nothing to be compared with them.

So eagerly the Utopians prosecute the injuries done to their friends, yea, in money matters; and not their own likewise. For if they by covin or guile be wiped beside their goods, so that no violence be done to their bodies, they wreak their anger by abstaining from occupying with that nation until they have made satisfaction; not for because they set less store by their own citizens than by their friends; but that they take the loss of their friends' money more heavily than the loss of their own: because that their friends' merchantmen, forasmuch as that they lose is their own private goods, sustain great damage by the loss; but their own citizens lose nothing but of the common goods and of that which was at home plentiful and almost superfluous, else had it not been sent forth; therefore no man feeleth the loss. And for this cause they think it too cruel an act to revenge that loss with the death of many; the incommodity of the which loss no man feeleth neither in his life, neither in his living. But if it chance that any of their men in any other country be maimed or killed, whether it be done by a common or a private counsel; knowing and trying out the truth of the matter by their ambassadors, unless the offenders be rendered unto them in recompense of the injury, they will not be appeased;

wiped beside = cheated of

but incontinent they proclaim war against them. The offenders yielded they punish either with death or with bondage.

They be not only sorry but also ashamed to achieve the victory with much bloodshed, counting it great folly to buy precious wares too dear. They rejoice and avaunt themselves if they vanquish and oppress their enemies by craft and deceit; and for that act they make a general triumph and as if the matter were manfully handled, they set up a pillar of stone in the place where they so vanquished their enemies in token of the victory. For then they glory, then they boast and crack that they have played the men indeed, when they have so overcome as no other living creature but only man could, that is to say, by the might and puissance of wit. For with bodily strength (say they) bears, lions, boars, dogs, wolves, and other wild beasts do fight; and as the most part of them do pass us in strength and fierce courage, so in wit and reason we be much stronger than they all.

Their chief and principal purpose in war is to obtain that thing which if they had before obtained, they would not have moved battle. But if that be not possible they take so cruel vengeance of them which be in the fault that ever after they be afeared to do the like. This is their chief and principal intent, which they immediately and first of all prosecute and set forward; but yet so that they be more circumspect in avoiding and eschewing jeopardies than they be desirous of praise and renown. Therefore immediately after that war is once solemnly denounced, they procure many proclamations signed with their own common seal, to be set up privily at one time in their enemy's land in places most frequented. In these proclamations they promise great rewards to him that will kill their enemy's prince; and somewhat less gifts, but them very great also, for every head of them whose names be in the said proclamations contained. They be those whom they count their chief adversaries, next unto the prince. Whatsoever is prescribed unto him that killeth any of the proclaimed persons, that is doubled to him that bringeth any of the same to them alive: yea, and to the proclaimed persons themselves, if they will change their minds and come in to them, taking their parts, they proffer the same great rewards with pardon and surety of their lives.

Therefore it quickly cometh to pass that they have all other men in suspicion, and be unfaithful and mistrusting among themselves one to another, living in great fear and in no less jeopardy. For it is well known that divers times the most part of them, and specially the prince himself, hath been betrayed of them in whom they put their most hope and trust. So that there is no manner of act nor deed that gifts and rewards do not enforce men unto. And in rewards they keep no measure; but remembering and considering into how great hazard and jeopardy they call them, endeavor themselves to recompense the greatness of the danger with like great benefits. And therefore they promise not only wonderful great abundance of gold, but also lands of great revenues, lying in most safe places among their friends. And their promises they perform faithfully, without any fraud or vocin.

This custom of buying and selling adversaries among other people is disallowed, as a cruel act of a base and a cowardish mind. But they in this behalf think themselves much praiseworthy, as who like wise men by this means dispatch great wars without any battle or skirmish. Yea, they count it also a deed of pity and mercy, because that by the death of a few offenders the lives of a great number of innocents, as well of their own men as also of their enemies, be ransomed and saved, which in fighting should have been slain. For they do no less pity the base and common sort of their enemies' people than they do their own, knowing that they be driven to war against their wills by the furious madness of their princes and heads.

If by none of these means the matter go forward as they would have it, then they procure occasions of debate and dissension to be spread among their enemies, as by bringing the prince's brother or some of the noblemen in hope to obtain the kingdom. If this way prevail not, then they raise up the people that be next neighbors and borderers to their enemies and them they set in their necks under the color of some old title of right, such as kings do never lack. To them they promise their help and aid in their war; and as for money they give them abundance, but of their own citizens they send to them few or none; whom they make so much of and love so entirely that they would not be willing to change any of them for their adversary's prince. But their gold and silver, because they kept it all for this only purpose, they lay it out frankly and freely; as who should live even as wealthily, if they had bestowed it every penny. Yea, and besides their riches which they keep at home, they have also an infinite treasure abroad, by reason that (as I said before) many nations be in their debt. Therefore they hire soldiers out of all countries and send them to battle, but chiefly of the Zapoletes. This people is five hundred miles from Utopia eastward. They be hideous, savage, and fierce, dwelling in wild woods and high mountains,

Zapoletes; from Ζαπωλ ῆται = readily sold

where they were bred and brought up. They be of an hard nature, able to abide and sustain heat, cold and labor; abhorring from all delicate dainties, occupying no husbandry nor tillage of the ground, homely and rude both in the building of their houses and in their apparel; given unto no goodness, but only to the breed and bringing up of cattle. The most part of their living is by hunting and stealing. They be born only to war, which they diligently and earnestly seek for; and when they have gotten it, they be wonders glad thereof. They go forth of their country in great companies together, and whosoever lacketh soldiers, there they proffer their service for small wages. This is only the craft that they have to get their living by. They maintain their life by seeking their death. For them whomwith they be in wages, they fight hardily, fiercely, and faithfully; but they bind themselves for no certain time. But upon this condition they enter into bonds that the next day they will take part with the other side for greater wages, and the next day after that they will be ready to come back again for a little more money. There be few wars thereaway wherein is not a great number of them in both parties. Therefore it daily chanceth that nigh kinsfolk, which were hired together on one part and there very friendly and familiarly used themselves one with another, shortly after, being separate into contrary parts, run one against another enviously and fiercely; and forgetting both kindred and friendship, thrust their swords one in another, and that for none other cause but that they be hired of contrary princes for a little money; which they do so highly regard and esteem that they will easily be provoked to change parts for a halfpenny more wages by the day. So quickly they have taken a smack in covet-

taken a smack in = acquired a taste for

ousness, which for all that is to them no profit; for that they get by fighting immediately they spend unthriftily and wretchedly in riot.

This people fight for the Utopians against all nations, because they give them greater wages than any other nation will. For the Utopians, like as they seek good men to use well, so they seek these evil and vicious men to abuse; whom when need requireth with promises of great rewards they put forth into great jeopardies, from whence the most part of them never cometh again to ask their rewards. But to them that remain on live they pay *on live = alive* that which they promised faithfully, that they may be the more willing to put themselves in like dangers another time. Nor the Utopians pass not how many of them they bring to destruction; for they believe that they should do a very good deed for all mankind if they could rid out of the world all that foul, stinking den of that most wicked and cursed people.

Next unto these they use the soldiers of them whom they fight for; and then the help of their other friends; and last of all they join to their own citizens, among whom they give to one of tried virtue and prowess the rule, governance, and conduction of the whole army. Under him they appoint two other; which whiles he is safe be both private and out of office, but if he be taken or slain, the one of the other two succeedeth him, as it were by inheritance. And if the second miscarry then the third taketh his room; lest that (as the chance of battle is uncertain and doubtful), the jeopardy or death of the captain should bring the whole army in hazard. They choose soldiers out of every city those which put forth themselves willingly; for they thrust no man forth into war against his will, because they believe if any man be

fearful and faint-hearted of nature he will not only do
no manful and hardy act himself but also be occasion of
cowardness to his fellows. But if any battle be made
against their own country, then they put these cowards,
so that they be strong-bodied, in ships among other,
bold-hearted men; or else they dispose them upon the
walls, from whence they may not fly. Thus, what for
shame that their enemies be at hand and what for because
they be without hope of running away, they forget all
fear. And many times extreme necessity turneth cowardness into prowess and manliness.

But as none of them is thrust forth of his country into
war against his will, so women that be willing to accom-
pany their husbands in times of war be not prohibited
or stopped. Yea, they provoke and exhort them to it
with praises. And in set field the wives do stand every
one by her own husband's side. Also every man is compassed next about with his own children, kinsfolks, and
alliance; that they whom nature chiefly moveth to mutual succor thus standing together may help one another.
It is a great reproach and dishonesty for the husband to
come home without his wife, or the wife without her
husband, or the son without his father. And therefore
if the other part stick so hard by it that the battle come to
their hands, it is fought with great slaughter and bloodshed, even to the utter destruction of both parts. For as
they make all the means and shifts that may be to keep
themselves from the necessity of fighting so that they
may dispatch the battle by their hired soldiers, so when
there is no remedy but that they must needs fight themselves, then they do as courageously fall to it as, before,
whiles they might, they did wisely avoid it. Nor they
be not most fierce at the first brunt; but in continuance

by little and little their fierce courage encreaseth, with
so stubborn and obstinate minds that they will rather die
than give back an inch. For that surety of living which
every man hath at home, being joined with no careful
anxiety or remembrance how their posterity shall live
after them (for this pensiveness oftentimes breaketh and
abateth courageous stomachs) maketh them stout and
hardy and disdainful to be conquered. Moreover, their
knowledge in chivalry and feats of arms putteth them
in a good hope. Finally, the wholesome and virtuous
opinions wherein they were brought up even from their
childhood, partly through learning and partly through
the good ordinances and laws of their weal public,
augment and encrease their manful courage; by reason
whereof they neither set so little store by their lives
that they will rashly and unadvisedly cast them away,
nor they be not so far in lewd and fond love therewith
that they will shamefully covet to keep them when
honesty biddeth leave them.

When the battle is hottest and in all places most fierce
and fervent, a band of chosen and picked young men,
which be sworn to live and die together, take upon
them to destroy their adversary's captain. Him they
invade, now with privy wiles, now by open strength.
At him they strike both near and far off. He is assailed
with a long and a continual assault, fresh men still coming in the wearied men's places. And seldom it chanceth
(unless he save himself by flying) that he is not either
slain or else taken prisoner and yielded to his enemies
alive. If they win the field, they persecute not their
enemies with the violent rage of slaughter, for they had
rather take them alive than kill them. Neither they do
so follow the chase and pursuit of their enemies but they

leave behind them one part of their host in battle array under their standards; insomuch that if all their whole army be discomfited and overcome, saving the rearward, and that they therewith achieve the victory, then they had rather let all their enemies scape than to follow them out of array. For they remember it hath chanced unto themselves more than once: the whole power and strength of their host being vanquished and put to flight, whiles their enemies rejoicing in the victory have persecuted them flying, some one way and some another, few of their men lying in an ambush, there ready at all occasions, have suddenly risen upon them thus dispersed and scattered out of array and through presumption of safety unadvisedly pursuing the chase, and have incontinent changed the fortune of the whole battle, and spite of their teeth wresting out of their hands the sure and undoubted victory, being a little before conquered, have for their part conquered the conquerors.

It is hard to say whether they be craftier in laying an ambush or wittier in avoiding the same. You would think they intend to fly, when they mean nothing less; and contrariwise, when they go about that purpose you would believe it were the least part of their thought. For if they perceive themselves either overmatched in number or closed in too narrow a place, then they remove their camp either in the night season with silence, or by some policy they deceive their enemies; or in the daytime they retire back so softly that it is no less jeopardy to meddle with them when they give back than when they press on. They fence and fortify their camp surely with a deep and a broad trench. The earth thereof is cast inward. Nor they do not set drudges and slaves awork about it: it is done by the hands of the soldiers themselves. All the whole army worketh upon it except them that watch in harness before the trench for sudden adventures. Therefore, by the labor of so many, a large trench closing in a great compass of ground is made in less time than any man would believe.

Their armor or harness which they wear is sure and strong to receive strokes and handsome for all movings and gestures of the body, insomuch that it is not unwieldy to swim in. For in the discipline of their warfare, among other feats they learn to swim in harness. Their weapons be arrows afar off, which they shoot both strongly and surely; not only footmen but also horsemen. At hand strokes they use not swords but pole-axes, which be mortal, as well in sharpness as in weight, both for foins and down strokes. Engines for war they devise *foins = thrusts* and invent wonders wittily; which when they be made they keep very secret, lest if they should be known before need require, they should be but laughed at and serve to no purpose. But in making them hereunto they have chief respect that they be both easy to be carried and handsome to be moved and turned about.

Truce taken with their enemies for a short time they do so firmly and faithfully keep that they will not break it; no, not though they be thereunto provoked. They do not waste nor destroy their enemies' land with foragings, nor they burn not up their corn. Yea, they save it as much as may be from being overrun and trodden down, either with men or horses; thinking that it groweth for their own use and profit. They hurt no man that is unarmed, unless he be an espial. All cities that be yielded unto them, they defend; and such as they win by force of assault, they neither despoil nor sack. But them that withstood and dissuaded the yielding up of the same they put to death; the other soldiers they punish with bondage. All the weak multitude they leave untouched. If they know that any citizens counselled to yield and render up the city, to them they give part of the condemned men's goods. The residue they distribute and give freely among them whose help they had in the same war, for none of themselves taketh any portion of the prey.

But when the battle is finished and ended they put their friends to never a penny cost of all the charges that they were at but lay it upon their necks that be conquered. Them they burden with the whole charge of their expenses, which they demand of them partly in money, to be kept for like use of battle, and partly in lands of great revenues, to be paid unto them yearly forever. Such revenues they have now in many countries; which by little and little rising of divers and sundry causes, be encreased above seven hundred thousand ducats by the year. Thither they send forth some of their citizens as lieutenants, to live there sumptuously like men of honor and renown; and yet, this notwithstanding, much money is saved, which cometh to the common treasury, unless it so chance that they had rather trust the country with the money; which many times they do so long until they have need to occupy it. And it seldom happeneth that they demand all. Of these lands they assign part unto them which at their request and exhortation put themselves in such jeopardies as I spake of before. If any prince stir up war against them, intending to invade their land, they meet him incontinent out of their own borders with great power and strength; for they never lightly make war in their own country. Nor they be never brought into so extreme necessity as to take help out of foreign lands into their own island.

Of the Religions in Utopia.

THERE be divers kinds of religion, not only in sundry parts of the island, but also in divers places of every city. Some worship for God the sun, some the moon, some some other of the planets. There be that give worship to a man that was once of excellent virtue or of famous glory, not only as God, but also as the chiefest and highest God. But the most and the wisest part (rejecting all these) believe that there is a certain godly power unknown, everlasting, incomprehensible, inexplicable, far above the capacity and reach of man's wit, dispersed throughout all the world, not in bigness, but in virtue and power. Him they call the father of all. To him alone they attribute the beginnings, the encreasings, the proceedings, the changes, and the ends of all things. Neither they give divine honors to any other than to him.

Yea, all the other also, though they be in divers opinions, yet in this point they agree altogether with the wisest sort in believing that there is one chief and principal God, the maker and ruler of the whole world; whom they all commonly in their country language call Mythra. But in this they disagree, that among some he is counted one, and among some another. For every one of them, whatsoever that is which he taketh for the chief God, thinketh it to be the very same nature, to whose only divine might and majesty the sum and sovereignty of all things, by the consent of all people, is attributed and given. Howbeit, they all begin by little and little to forsake and fall from this variety of superstitions and to agree together in that religion which seemeth by reason to pass and excel the residue. And it is not to be doubted but all the other would long ago have been abolished, but that whatsoever unprosperous thing happened to any of them as he was minded to change his religion, the fearfulness of people did take it not as a thing coming by chance but as sent from God out of heaven, as though the God whose honor he was forsaking would revenge that wicked purpose against him.

But after they heard us speak of the name of Christ, of his doctrine, laws, miracles, and of the no less wonderful constancy of so many martyrs, whose blood willingly shed brought a great number of nations throughout all parts of the world into their sect; you will not believe with how glad minds they agreed unto the same, whether it were by the secret inspiration of God, or else for that they thought it next unto that opinion which among them is counted the chiefest. Howbeit, I think this was no small help and furtherance in the matter, that they heard us say that Christ instituted among his all things common, and that the same community doth yet remain amongst the rightest Christian companies. Verily, howsoever it come to pass, many of them consented together in our religion and were washed in the holy water of baptism.

But because among us four (for no more of us was left alive, two of our company being dead) there was no priest, which I am right sorry for, they being entered and instructed in all other points of our religion, lack only those sacraments which here none but priests do minister. Howbeit, they understand and perceive them and be very desirous of the same. Yea, they reason and dispute the matter earnestly among themselves, whether, without the sending of a Christian bishop, one chosen out of their own people may receive the order of priest-

hood. And truly they were minded to choose one, but
at my departure from them they had chosen none. They
also which do not agree to Christ's religion fear no man
from it, nor speak against any man that hath received
it, saving that one of our company in my presence was
sharply punished. He, as soon as he was baptized, began
against our wills, with more earnest affection than wisdom, to reason of Christ's religion, and began to wax so
hot in his matter that he did not only prefer our religion
before all other, but also did utterly despise and condemn all other, calling them profane and the followers
of them wicked and devilish and the children of everlasting damnation. When he had thus long reasoned the
matter, they laid hold on him, accused him, and condemned him into exile; not as a despiser of religion,
but as a seditious person and a raiser up of dissension
among the people. For this is one of the ancientest laws
among them: that no man shall be blamed for reasoning
in the maintenance of his own religion.

For King Utopus, even at the first beginning, hearing
that the inhabitants of the land were before his coming
thither at continual dissension and strife among themselves for their religions; perceiving also that this common dissension, whiles every several sect took several
parts in fighting for their country, was the only occasion
of his conquest over them all; as soon as he had gotten
the victory, first of all he made a decree that it should be
lawful for every man to favor and follow what religion
he would, and that he might do the best he could to bring
other to his opinion; so that he did it peaceably, gently,
quietly, and soberly, without hasty and contentious re-
buking and inveighing against other. If he could not by
fair and gentle speech induce them unto his opinion, yet

he should use no kind of violence and refrain from displeasant and seditious words. To him that would vehemently and fervently in this cause strive and contend, was decreed banishment or bondage.

This law did King Utopus make, not only for the maintenance of peace, which he saw through continual contention and mortal hatred utterly extinguished, but also because he thought this decree should make for the furtherance of religion; whereof he durst define and determine nothing unadvisedly, as doubting whether God, desiring manifold and divers sorts of honor, would inspire sundry men with sundry kinds of religion. And this surely he thought a very unmeet and foolish thing and a point of arrogant presumption, to compel all other by violence and threatenings to agree to the same that thou believest to be true. Furthermore though there be one religion which alone is true, and all other vain and superstitious, yet did he well foresee (so that the matter were handled with reason and sober modesty), that the *the own = its own* truth of the own power would at the last issue out and come to light. But if contention and debate in that behalf should continually be used, as the worst men be most obstinate and stubborn and in their evil opinion most constant, he perceived that then the best and holiest religion would be trodden under foot and destroyed by most vain superstitions; even as good corn is by thorns and weeds overgrown and choked. Therefore all this matter he left undiscussed and gave to every man free liberty and choice to believe what he would, saving that he earnestly and straitly charged them that no man should conceive so vile and base an opinion of the dignity of man's nature as to think that the souls do die and perish with the body or that the world runneth at all ad-

ventures, governed by no divine providence. And therefore they believe that after this life vices be extremely
punished and virtues bountifully rewarded. Him that
is of a contrary opinion they count not in the number
of men, as one that hath avaled the high nature of his
soul to the vileness of brute beasts' bodies; much less in
the number of their citizens, whose laws and ordinances,
if it were not for fear, he would nothing at all esteem.
For you may be sure that he will study either with craft
privily to mock, or else violently to break, the common
laws of his country, in whom remaineth no further fear
than of the laws nor no further hope than of the body.
Wherefore he that is thus minded is deprived of all
honors, excluded from all offices, and reject from all
common administrations in the weal public. And thus
he is of all sort despised as of an unprofitable and of a
base and vile nature. Howbeit, they put him to no punishment, because they be persuaded that it is in no man's
power to believe what he list. No, nor they constrain
him not with threatenings to dissemble his mind and
show countenance contrary to his thought; for deceit
and falsehood and all manner of lies, as next unto fraud,
they do marvelously detest and abhor. But they suffer
him not to dispute in his opinion; and that only among
the common people; for else, apart among the priests
and men of gravity, they do not only suffer but also
exhort him to dispute and argue, hoping that at the last
that madness will give place to reason.

There be also other, and of them no small number,
which be not forbidden to speak their minds, as ground-
ing their opinion upon some reason, being in their living
neither evil nor vicious. Their heresy is much contrary
to the other, for they believe that the souls of brute

beasts be immortal and everlasting, but nothing to be compared with ours in dignity, neither ordained and predestinate to like felicity. For all they believe certainly and surely that man's bliss shall be so great that they do mourn and lament every man's sickness but no man's death, unless it be one whom they see depart from his life carefully and against his will. For this they take for a very evil token, as though the soul, being in despair and vexed in conscience through some privy and secret fore-feeling of the punishment now at hand, were afeared to depart; and they think he shall not be welcome to God which when he is called runneth not to him gladly, but is drawn by force and sore against his will. They therefore that see this kind of death do abhor it, and them that so die they bury with sorrow and silence; and when they have prayed God to be merciful to the soul and mercifully to pardon the infirmities thereof, they cover the dead corpse with earth.

Contrariwise, all that depart merrily and full of good hope, for them no man mourneth, but followeth the hearse with joyful singing, commending the souls to God with great affection; and at the last, not with mourning sorrow but with a great reverence, they burn the bodies; and in the same place they set up a pillar of stone with the dead man's titles therein graved. When they be come home they rehearse his virtuous manners and his good deeds, but no part of his life is so oft or gladly talked of as his merry death. They think that this remembrance of their virtue and goodness doth vehemently provoke and enforce the quick to virtue; and that nothing can be more pleasant and acceptable to the dead, whom they suppose to be present among them when they talk of them, though to the dull and feeble eyesight of mortal

men they be invisible. For it were an unconvenient thing
that the blessed should not be at liberty to go whither
they would; and it were a point of great unkindness in
them to have utterly cast away the desire of visiting and
seeing their friends to whom they were in their lifetime
joined by mutual love and charity, which in good men
after their death they count to be rather encreased than
diminished. They believe therefore that the dead be
presently conversant among the quick, as beholders and
witnesses of all their words and deeds. Therefore they
go more courageously to their business, as having a trust
and affiance in such overseers; and this same belief of the
present conversation of their forefathers and ancestors
among them feareth them from all secret dishonesty.

They utterly despise and mock soothsayings and divinations of things to come by the flight or voices of birds,
and all other divinations of vain superstition which in
other countries be in great observation. But they highly
esteem and worship miracles that come by no help of
nature as works and witnesses of the present power of
God, and such they say do chance there very often. And
sometimes in great and doubtful matters by common
intercession and prayers they procure and obtain them
with a sure hope and confidence and a steadfast belief.

They think that the contemplation of nature and the
praise thereof coming is to God a very acceptable honor.
Yet there be many so earnestly bent and affectioned to
religion that they pass no thing for learning, nor give
their minds to no knowledge of things. But idleness they
utterly forsake and eschew, thinking felicity after this
life to be gotten and obtained by busy labors and good
exercises. Some therefore of them attend upon the sick,
some amend highways, cleanse ditches, repair bridges,

dig turfs, gravel, and stones, fell and cleave wood, bring wood, corn, and other things into the cities in carts; and serve not only in common works, but also in private labors, as servants, yea, more than bondmen. For whatsoever unpleasant, hard, and vile work is anywhere, from the which labor, loathsomeness, and desperation doth *fray = frighten* fray other, all that they take upon them willingly and gladly; procuring quiet and rest to other, remaining in continual work and labor themselves, not embraiding others therewith. They neither reprove other men's lives nor glory in their own. These men, the more serviceable they behave themselves, the more they be honored of all men.

Yet they be divided into two sects. The one is of them that live single and chaste, abstaining not only from the company of women but also from the eating of flesh, and some of them from all manner of beasts; which, utterly rejecting the pleasures of this present life as hurtful, be all wholly set upon the desire of the life to come; by watching and sweating, hoping shortly to obtain it, being in the mean season merry and lusty. The other sect is no less desirous of labor, but they embrace matrimony; not despising the solace thereof, thinking that they cannot be discharged of their bounden duties towards nature without labor and toil nor towards their native country without procreation of children. They abstain from no pleasure that doth nothing hinder them from labor. They love the flesh of four-footed beasts, because they believe that by that meat they be made hardier and stronger to work. The Utopians count this sect the wiser, but the other the holier; which, in that they prefer single life before matrimony, and that sharp life before an easier life, if herein they grounded upon reason, they would mock them; but now, forasmuch as they say they be led to it by religion, they honor and worship them. And these be they whom in their language by a peculiar name they call buthrescas, the which word by interpretation signifieth to us, men of religion, or religious men.

They have priests of exceeding holiness, and therefore very few; for there be but thirteen in every city, according to the number of their churches, saving when they go forth to battle; for then seven of them go forth with the army, in whose steads so many new be made at home. But the other, at their return home, again re-enter every one into his own place. They that be above the number, until such time as they succeed into the places of the other at their dying, be in the mean season continually in company with the bishop, for he is the chief head of them all. They be chosen of the people as the other magistrates be, by secret voices for the avoiding of strife. After their election they be consecrate of their own company. They be overseers of all divine matters, orderers of religions, and as it were judges and masters of manners; and it is a great dishonesty and shame to be rebuked or spoken to by any of them for dissolute and incontinent living.

But as it is their office to give good exhortations and counsel, so it is the duty of the prince and the other magistrates to correct and punish offenders, saving that the priests, whom they find exceeding vicious livers, them they excommunicate from having any interest in divine matters. And there is almost no punishment among them more feared; for they run in very great infamy and be inwardly tormented with a secret fear of religion and shall not long scape free with their bodies; for unless they by quick repentance approve the amendment of their lives to the priests, they be taken and punished of the council as wicked and irreligious.

Both childhood and youth is instructed and taught of them. Nor they be not more diligent to instruct them in learning than in virtue and good manners; for they use with very great endeavor and diligence to put into the heads of their children whiles they be yet tender and pliant good opinions and profitable for the conservation of their weal public; which, when they be once rooted in children, do remain with them all their life after and be wonders profitable for the defence and maintenance of the state of the commonwealth, which never decayeth but through vices rising of evil opinions.

The priests, unless they be women (for that kind is not excluded from priesthood; howbeit few be chosen, and none but widows and old women) — the men priests, I say, take to their wives the chiefest women in all their country; for to no office among the Utopians is more honor and pre-eminence given, insomuch that if they commit any offence they be under no common judgment but be left only to God and themselves; for they think it not lawful to touch him with man's hand, be he never so vicious, which after so singular a sort was dedicate and consecrate to God as a holy offering. This manner may they easily observe because they have so few priests and do choose them with such circumspection; for it scarcely ever chanceth that the most virtuous among virtuous, which in respect only of his virtue is advanced to so high a dignity, can fall to vice and wickedness. And if it should chance indeed (as man's nature is mutable and frail), yet by reason they be so few and promoted to no might nor power, but only honor, it were not to be feared that any great damage by them should happen and ensue to the commonwealth. They have so rare and few priests, lest, if the honor were communicate to many, the dignity of the order, which among them now is so highly esteemed, should run in contempt; specially because they think it hard to find many so good as to be meet for that dignity, to the execution and discharge whereof it is not sufficient to be endued with mean virtues.

Furthermore, these priests be not more esteemed of their own countrymen than they be of foreign and strange countries; which thing may hereby plainly appear, and I think also that this is the cause of it: for whiles the armies be fighting together in open field, they a little beside, not far off, kneel upon their knees in their hallowed vestments, holding up their hands to heaven; praying, first of all for peace, next for victory of their own part, but to neither part a bloody victory. If their host get the upper hand, they run into the main battle and restrain their own men from slaying and cruelly pursuing their vanquished enemies, which enemies, if they do but see them and speak to them, it is enough for the safeguard of their lives; and the touching of their clothes defendeth and saveth all their goods from ravin and spoil. This thing hath advanced them to so great worship and true majesty among all nations that many times they have as well preserved their own citizens from the cruel force of their enemies as they have their enemies from the furious rage of their own men; for it is well known that when their own army hath reculed *reculed = retreated* and in despair turned back and run away, their enemies fiercely pursuing with slaughter and spoil, then the priests coming between have stayed the murder and parted both the hosts; so that peace hath been made and concluded between both parts upon equal and indifferent conditions. For there was never any nation so fierce, so cruel and rude but they had them in such reverence that they counted their bodies hallowed and sanctified, and therefore not to be violently and unreverently touched.

They keep holy day the first and the last day of every month and year; dividing the year into months, which they measure by the course of the moon, as they do the year by the course of the sun. The first days they call in their language Cynemernes, and the last Trapemernes; the which words may be interpreted primifest and finifest, or else in our speech first feast and last feast.

Their churches be very gorgeous, and not only of fine and curious workmanship, but also (which in the fewness of them was necessary) very wide and large and able to receive a great company of people; but they be all somewhat dark. Howbeit, that was not done through ignorance in building but, as they say, by the counsel of the priests, because they thought that overmuch light doth disperse men's cogitations, whereas in dim and doubtful light they be gathered together, and more earnestly fixed upon religion and devotion; which because it is not there of one sort among all men; and yet all the kinds and fashions of it, though they be sundry and manifold, agree together in the honor of the divine nature, as going divers ways to one end; therefore nothing is seen nor heard in the churches which seemeth not to agree indifferently with them all. If there be a distinct kind of sacrifice, peculiar to any several sect, that they execute at home in their own houses. The common sacrifices be so ordered that they be no derogation nor prejudice to any of the private sacrifices and religions.

Therefore no image of any god is seen in the church, to the intent it may be free for every man to conceive God by their religion after what likeness and similitude they will. They call upon no peculiar name of God, but only Mythra; in the which word they all agree together in one nature of the divine majesty, whatsoever it be. No prayers be used but such as every man may boldly pronounce without the offending of any sect.

They come therefore to the church the last day of every month and year, in the evening, yet fasting, there to give thanks to God for that they have prosperously passed over the year or month whereof that holy day is the last day. The next day they come to the church early in the morning to pray to God that they may have good fortune and success all the new year or month which they do begin of that same holy day. But in the holy days that be the last days of the months and years, before they come to the church the wives fall down prostrate before their husbands' feet at home; and the children before the feet of their parents, confessing and acknowledging that they have offended either by some actual deed or by omission of their duty, and desire pardon for their offence. Thus if any cloud of privy displeasure was risen at home, by this satisfaction it is overblown, that they may be present at the sacrifices with pure and charitable minds, for they be afeared to come there with troubled consciences. Therefore, if they know themselves to bear any hatred or grudge towards any man, they presume not to come to the sacrifices before they have reconciled themselves and purged their consciences, for fear of great vengeance and punishment for their offence.

When they come thither the men go into the right side of the church and the women into the left side. There they place themselves in such order that all they which be of the male kind in every household sit before the goodman of the house, and they of the female kind before the goodwife. Thus it is foreseen that all their gestures and behaviors be marked and observed abroad of them by whose authority and discipline they be governed at home. This also they diligently see unto, that the younger evermore be coupled with his elder, lest, if children be joined together, they should pass over that time in childish wantonness wherein they ought principally to conceive a religious and devout fear towards God, which is the chief and almost the only incitation to virtue.

They kill no living beast in sacrifice, nor they think not that the merciful clemency of God hath delight in blood and slaughter; which hath given life to beasts to the intent they should live. They burn frankincense and other sweet savors, and light also a great number of wax candles and tapers; not supposing this gear to be anything available to the divine nature, as neither the prayers of men; but this unhurtful and harmless kind of worship pleaseth them, and by these sweet savors and lights and other such ceremonies men feel themselves secretly lifted up and encouraged to devotion with more willing and fervent hearts. The people weareth in the church white apparel: the priest is clothed in changeable colors, which in workmanship be excellent but in stuff not very precious, for their vestments be neither embroidered with gold nor set with precious stones, but they be wrought so finely and cunningly with divers feathers of fowls that the estimation of no costly stuff is able to countervail the price of the work. Furthermore, in these birds' feathers and in the due order of them which is observed in their setting, they say is contained certain divine mysteries, the interpretation whereof known, which is diligently taught by the priests, they be put in remembrance of the bountiful benefits of God towards them and of the love and honor which of their behalf is due to God, and also of their duties one toward another.

When the priest first cometh out of the vestry thus apparelled, they fall down incontinent every one reverently to the ground, with so still silence on every part that the very fashion of the thing striketh into them a certain fear of God, as though he were there personally present. When they have lain a little space on the ground the priest giveth them a sign for to rise. Then they sing praises unto God, which they intermix with instruments of music, for the most part of other fashions than these that we use in this part of the world. And like as some of ours be much sweeter than theirs, so some of theirs do far pass ours. But in one thing doubtless they go exceeding far beyond us; for all their music, both that they play upon instruments and that they sing with man's voice, doth so resemble and express natural affections, the sound and tune is so applied and made agreeable to the thing, that whether it be a prayer or else a ditty of gladness, of patience, of trouble, of mourning, or of anger, the fashion of the melody doth so represent the meaning of the thing that it doth wonderfully move, stir, pierce, and inflame the hearers' minds.

At the last the people and the priest together rehearse solemn prayers in words expressly pronounced, so made that every man may privately apply to himself that which is commonly spoken of all. In these prayers every man recognizeth and knowledgeth God to be his maker, his governor, and the principal cause of all other goodness, thanking him for so many benefits received at his hand, but namely that through the favor of God he hath chanced into that public weal which is most happy and wealthy and hath chosen that religion which he hopeth to be most true; in the which thing, if he do anything err, or if there be any other better than either of them is, being more acceptable to God, he desireth him that he will of his goodness let him have knowledge thereof, as one that is ready to follow what way soever he will lead him: but if this form and fashion of a commonwealth be best and his own religion most true and perfect, then he desireth God to give him a constant steadfastness in the same and to bring all other people to the same order of living and to the same opinion of God; unless there be anything that in this diversity of religions doth delight his unsearchable pleasure. To be short, he prayeth him that after his death he may come to him; but how soon or late, that he dare not assign or determine. Howbeit, if it might stand with his majesty's pleasure, he would be much gladder to die a painful death and so to go to God than by long living in worldly prosperity to be away from him.When this prayer is said they fall down to the ground again, and a little after they rise up and go to dinner. And the residue of the day they pass over in plays and exercise of

chivalry =
military training   chivalry.

Now I have declared and described unto you as truly as I could the form and order of that commonwealth which verily in my judgment is not only the

best but also that which alone of good right may claim
and take upon it the name of a commonwealth or public
weal. For in other places they speak still of the commonwealth, but every man procureth his own private
wealth. Here where nothing is private, the common
affairs be earnestly looked upon. And truly on both
parts they have good cause so to do as they do. For in
other countries who knoweth not that he shall starve
for hunger, unless he make some several provision for
himself, though the commonwealth flourish never so
much in riches? And therefore he is compelled, even
of very necessity, to have regard to himself rather than
to the people, that is to say, to other. Contrariwise,
there where all things be common to every man, it is
not to be doubted that any man shall lack anything
necessary for his private uses, so that the common storehouses and barns be sufficiently stored. For there nothing is distributed after a niggish sort, neither there is
any poor man or beggar; and though no man have anything, yet every man is rich. For what can be more rich
than to live joyfully and merrily without all grief and
pensiveness, not caring for his own living nor vexed
or troubled with his wife's importunate complaints,
not dreading poverty to his son nor sorrowing for his
daughter's dowry? Yea, they take no care at all for the
living and wealth of themselves and all theirs, of their
wives, their children, their nephews, their children's
children, and all the succession that ever shall follow in
their posterity. And yet, besides this, there is no less
provision for them that were once laborers and be now
weak and impotent than for them that do now labor
and take pain.

Here now would I see if any man dare be so bold as

to compare with this equity the justice of other nations, among whom I forsake God if I can find any sign or token of equity and justice. For what justice is this that a rich goldsmith or an usurer or, to be short, any of them which either do nothing at all, or else that which they do is such that it is not very necessary to the commonwealth, should have a pleasant and a wealthy living, either by idleness or by unnecessary business? when in the meantime poor laborers, carters, ironsmiths, carpenters, and plowmen, by so great and continual toil as drawing and bearing beasts be scant able to sustain, and again so necessary toil that without it no commonwealth were able to continue and endure one year, do yet get so hard and poor a living and live so wretched and miserable a life that the state and condition of the laboring beasts may seem much better and wealthier; for they be not put to so continual labor, nor their living is not much worse; yea, to them much pleasanter, taking no thought in the mean season for the time to come. But these silly poor wretches be presently tormented with barren and unfruitful labor; and the remembrance of their poor, indigent, and beggarly old age killeth them up; for their daily wages is so little that it will not suffice for the same day, much less it yieldeth any overplus that may daily be laid up for the relief of old age.

Is not this an unjust and an unkind public weal, which giveth great fees and rewards to gentlemen, as they call them, and to goldsmiths, and to such other, which be either idle persons or else only flatterers and devisers of vain pleasures; and, of the contrary part, maketh no gentle provision for poor plowmen, colliers, laborers, carters, ironsmiths, and carpenters; without whom no commonwealth can continue? But when it hath abused the labors of their lusty and flowering age, at the last, when they be oppressed with old age and sickness, being needy, poor, and indigent of all things; then, forgetting their so many painful watchings, not remembering their so many and so great benefits, recompenseth and acquitteth them most unkindly with miserable death. And yet besides this the rich men not only by private fraud but also by common laws do every day pluck and snatch away from the poor some part of their daily living; so, whereas it seemed before unjust to recompense with unkindness their pains that have been beneficial to the public weal, now they have to this their wrong and unjust dealing (which is yet a much worse point) given the name of justice; yea, and that by force of a law.

Therefore when I consider and weigh in my mind all these commonwealths which nowadays anywhere do flourish, so God help me, I can perceive nothing but a certain conspiracy of rich men, procuring their own commodities under the name and title of the commonwealth. They invent and devise all means and crafts, first how to keep safely without fear of losing that they have unjustly gathered together; and next how to hire and abuse the work and labor of the poor for as little money as may be. These devices, when the rich men have decreed to be kept and observed for the commonwealth's sake, that is to say, for the wealth also of the poor people, then they be made laws. But these most wicked and vicious men, when they have by their unsatiable covetousness divided among themselves all those things which would have sufficed all men, yet how far be they from the wealth and felicity of the Utopian commonwealth? out of the which in that all the desire of money with the use thereof is utterly secluded and banished, how great a heap of cares is cut away? how great an occasion of wickedness and mischief is plucked up by the roots? For who knoweth not that fraud, theft, ravin, brawling, quarreling, brabbling, strife, chiding, contention, murder, treason, poisoning, which by daily punishments are rather revenged than refrained, do die when money dieth? And also that fear, grief, care, labors, and watchings do perish even the very same moment that money perisheth? Yea, poverty itself, which only seemed to lack money, if money were gone, it also would decrease and vanish away.

And that you may perceive this more plainly, consider with yourselves some barren and unfruitful year, wherein many thousands of people have starved for hunger. I dare be bold to say that in the end of that penury so much corn or grain might have been found in the rich men's barns, if they had been searched, as being divided among them whom famine and pestilence hath killed, no man at all should have felt that plague and penury. So easily might men get their living if that same worthy princess, Lady Money, did not alone stop up the way between us and our living; which, a God's name, was very excellently devised and invented that by her the way thereto should be opened. I am sure the rich men perceive this, nor they be not ignorant how much better it were to lack no necessary thing than to abound with over-much superfluity, to be rid out of innumerable cares and troubles than to be besieged with great riches. And I doubt not that either the respect of every man's private commodity, or else the authority of our saviour Christ (which for his great wisdom could not but know what were best, and for his inestimable goodness could not but counsel to that which he knew to be best) would have brought all the world long ago into the laws of this weal public, if it were not that one only beast, the princess and mother of all mischief, Pride, doth withstand and let it. She measureth not wealth and prosperity by her own commodities but by the miseries and incommodities of other. She would not by her good will be made a goddess, if there were no wretches left whom she might be lady over to mock and scorn; over whose miseries her felicity might shine, whose poverty she might vex, torment, and encrease by gorgeously setting forth her riches. This hell-hound creepeth into men's hearts and plucketh them back from entering the right path of life, and is so deeply rooted in men's breasts that she cannot be plucked out.

This form and fashion of a weal public, which I would gladly wish unto all nations, I am glad yet that it hath chanced to the Utopians; which have followed those institutions of life whereby they have laid such foundations of their commonwealth as shall continue and last, not only wealthily but also, as far as man's wit may judge and conjecture, shall endure forever. For seeing the chief causes of ambition and sedition with other vices be plucked up by the roots and abandoned, at home there can be no jeopardy of domestical dissension, which alone hath cast under foot and brought to naught the well-fortified and strongly-defenced wealth and riches of many cities. But forasmuch as perfect concord remaineth, and wholesome laws be executed at home, the envy of all foreign princes be not able to shake or move the empire, though they have many times long ago gone about to do it, being evermore driven back.

Thus when Raphael had made an end of his tale, though many things came to my mind which in the manners and laws of that people seemed to be instituted and founded of no good reason, not only in the fashion of their chivalry, and in their sacrifices and religions and in other of their laws, but also, yea and chiefly, in that which is the principal foundation of all their ordinances, that is to say, in the community of their life and living, without any occupying of money (by the which thing only all nobility, magnificence, worship, honor, and majesty, the true ornaments and honors, as the common opinion is, of a commonwealth, utterly be overthrown and destroyed); yet, because I knew that he was weary of talking, and was not sure whether he could abide that anything should be said against his mind, specially because I remembered that he had reprehended this fault in other, which be afeared lest they should seem not to be wise enough unless they could find some fault in other men's inventions; therefore I, praising both their institutions and his communication, took him by the hand and led him in to supper; saying that we would choose another time to weigh and examine the same matters, and to talk with him more at large therein; which would to God it might once come to pass. In the meantime, as I cannot agree and consent to all things that he said (being else without doubt a man singularly well learned and also in all worldly matters exactly and profoundly experienced) so must I needs confess and grant that many things be in the Utopian weal public which in our cities I may rather wish for than hope after.

Thus endeth the afternoon's talk of
Raphael Hythloday concerning
the laws and institutions
of the island of
Utopia.

To the Right Hon. Jerome Buslide

Provost of Arienum and Counsellor of the
Catholic King Charles, Peter Giles, citizen
of Antwerp, wisheth health and felicity:

THOMAS MORE, the singular ornament of this our age, as you yourself (right honorable Buslyde), can witness, to whom he is perfectly well known, sent unto me this other day *The Island of Utopia*, to very few as yet known but most worthy; which, as far excelling Plato's commonwealth, all people should be willing to know; specially of a man most eloquent so finely set forth, so cunningly painted out, and so evidently subject to the eye that as oft as I read it, methinketh that I see somewhat more than when I heard Raphael Hythloday himself (for I was present at that talk as well as Master More) uttering and pronouncing his own words. Yea, though the same man, according to his pure eloquence, did so open and declare the matter that he might plainly enough appear to report not things which he had learned of others only by hearsay but which he had with his own eyes presently seen and thoroughly viewed and wherein he had no small time been conversant and abiding; a man truly in mine opinion as touching the knowledge of regions, peoples, and worldly experience much passing, yea even the very famous and renowned traveller Ulysses, and indeed such a one as for the space of these eight hundred years past I think nature into the world brought not forth his like; in comparison of whom Vespucci may be thought to have seen nothing.

Moreover, whereas we be wont more effectually and pithily to declare and express things that we have seen than which we have but only heard, there was besides that in this man a certain peculiar grace and singular dexterity to describe and set forth a matter withal. Yet the selfsame things as oft as I behold and consider them drawn and painted out with Master More's pencil, I am therewith so moved, so delighted, so inflamed, and so rapt that sometimes methinks I am presently conversant, even in the island of Utopia. And I promise you, I can scant believe that Raphael himself by all that five years' space that he was in Utopia abiding saw there so much as here in Master More's description is to be seen and perceived; which description with so many wonders and miraculous things is replenished that I stand in great doubt whereat first and chiefly to muse or marvel, whether at the excellency of his perfect and sure memory which could well-nigh word by word rehearse so many things once only heard; or else at his singular prudence, who so well and wittily marked and bare away all the original causes and fountains (to the vulgar people commonly most unknown) whereof both issueth and springeth the mortal confusion and utter decay of a commonwealth and also the advancement and wealthy state of the same may rise and grow; or else at the efficacy and pith of his words, which in so fine a Latin style, with such force of eloquence hath couched together and comprised so many and divers matters, specially being a man continually encumbered with so many busy and trouble-

some cares, both public and private, as he is. Howbeit
all these things cause you little to marvel, right honorable Buslyde, for that you are familiarly and thoroughly
acquainted with the notable, yea almost divine, wit of
the man.

But now to proceed to other matters, I surely know
nothing needful or requisite to be adjoined unto his writings, only a metre of four verses written in the Utopian
tongue, which after Master More's departure Hythloday by chance showed me, that have I caused to be
added thereto, with the alphabet of the same nation, and
have also garnished the margent of the book with certain
notes. For, as touching the situation of the island, that
is to say, in what part of the world Utopia standeth, the
ignorance and lack whereof not a little troubleth and
grieveth Master More, indeed Raphael left not that un-
spoken of. Howbeit with very few words he lightly
touched it, incidentally by the way passing it over, as
meaning of likelihood to keep and reserve that to another
place; and the same, I wot not now, by a certain evil and
unlucky chance escaped us both. For when Raphael was
speaking thereof, one of Master More's servants came
to him and whispered in his ear; wherefore I being then
of purpose more earnestly addict to hear, one of the
company, by reason of cold, taken I think a shipboard,
coughed out so loud that he took from my hearing certain of his words. But I will never stint nor rest until I
have got the full and exact knowledge hereof; insomuch
that I will be able perfectly to instruct you, not only in
the longitude or true meridian of the island, but also in
the just latitude thereof, that is to say, in the sublevation
or height of the pole in that region, if our friend Hythloday be in safety and alive.

For we hear very uncertain news of him. Some report that he died in his journey homeward; some again affirm that he returned into his country, but partly for that he could not away with the fashions of his country folk and partly for that his mind and affection were altogether set and fixed upon Utopia, they say that he hath taken his voyage thitherward again.

Now as touching this, that the name of this island is nowhere found among the old and ancient cosmographers, this doubt Hythloday himself very well dissolved. For why it is possible enough (quoth he) that the name which it had in old time was afterward changed or else that they never had knowledge of this island, forasmuch as now in our time divers lands be found which to the old geographers were unknown.

Howbeit, what needeth it in this behalf to fortify the matter with arguments, seeing Master More is author hereof sufficient? But whereas he doubteth of the edition or imprinting of the book, indeed herein I both commend and also knowledge the man's modesty. Howbeit, unto me it seemeth a work most unworthy to be long suppressed and most worthy to go abroad into the hands of men, yea and under the title of your name to be published to the world; either because the singular endowments and qualities of Master More be to no man better known than to you or else because no man is more fit and meet than you with good counsels to further and advance the commonwealth, wherein you have many years already continued and travailed with great glory and commendation, both of wisdom and knowledge and also of integrity and uprightness.

Thus, O liberal supporter of good learning and flower of this our time, I bid you most heartily well to fare.

At Antwerp, 1516, the first day of November.

The Utopian Alphabet.

ⓞⴱⴲⴳⴴⵔⵕⴳⵖⵗⴳⴹⵚⵛⵜ◻ⴱⵡⵢⵣ◲

a b c d e f g h i k l m n o p q r s t u x y

A meter of iiii verses in the Utopian tongue.

Utopos   ha   Boccas   peula

ⴱⵡⵔⵕⴳ ⴳⵛ ⴲⵚⵘⵘⵛⴱ ⵔⴳⴱⵚⵛ

chama   polta   chamaan.

ⵘⴳⵛⵗⴳ ⵔⵚⴱⵡⵛ ⵘⴳⵛⵗⵗⵚⵕ·

Bargol   he maglomi   baccan

ⴲⵛ◻ⵕⵚⴱ ⴳⴳ ⵗⵛⵕⴱⵚⵗ ⴲⵛⵘⵘⵛⵕ

soma   gymnosophaon.

ⴱⵚⵗ ⵕ◲ⵗⵕⵒⵘⴱⵔⴳⵛⵒⵕ·

Agrama   gymnosophon   labarem

ⵗⵕ◻ⵛⵗ ⵕ◲ⵗⵕⵒⵘⴱⵔⴳⵒⵕ ⵚⵛⴲⵛ◻ⴳⵗ

bacha   bodamilomin.

ⴲⵛⵘⴳⵗ ⴲⵚⵗⵗⵕⵘⵚⵚⵛ◻ⵕ·

Voluala   barchin   heman la

ⴱⵚⴲⴱⵗⵚⵛ ⴲⵛ◻ⵘⴳⵗⵒ ⴳⴳⵕⵒ ⴲⵛ

lauoluola   dramme   pagloni.

ⴲⵛⴲⵚⴲⵚⴲⴲⵚⵛ ⵘ◻ⵗⵕⵕⴳ ⵔⵗⵒⴳⵒⵕⴳ·

Which verses the translator, according to his simple
knowledge, and mean understanding in the Utopian
tongue, has thus rudely Englished.

My king and conqueror, Utopus by name,
A prince of much renown and immortal fame,
Hath made me an isle that erst no island was,
Full fraught with worldly wealth, with pleasure & solace.
I one of all other without philosophy
Have shaped for man a philosophical city.
As mine I am nothing dangerous to impart,
So better to receive I am ready with all my heart.

The pages of this edition of UTOPIA faithfully copy those of the edition designed by BRUCE ROGERS *for The Limited Editions Club. The text has been set in fourteen-point Monotype Janson, and the decorations reproduce those arranged by BR from printers' ornaments. The composition and printing were done at The Thistle Press; the binding is by The Russell-Rutter Company.*